THE ROCKWELL LECTURES

The Rice Institute · Houston

The Making
of Modern Mind

by

LEONARD CARMICHAEL

Secretary, Smithsonian Institution

HOUSTON

THE ELSEVIER PRESS

1956

SOLE DISTRIBUTORS FOR CONTINENTAL EUROPE:

Elsevier Publishing Company
110 Spuistraat, Amsterdam C.

FOR THE BRITISH COMMONWEALTH EXCEPT CANADA:

Cleaver-Hume Press, Ltd.
31, Wright's Lane, Kensington, London, W. 8.

Library of Congress Catalog Card Number 55-10889

PRINTED IN THE NETHERLANDS BY
N. V. DRUKKERIJ G. J. THIEME

INTRODUCTION

The Rockwell Lectures of the Rice Institute are made possible by the Rockwell Fund, Inc. A series of three lectures annually, the lectures were inaugurated by Sir Robert A. Falconer in April, 1938. Later lectures have been given by Dr. Harris Elliot Kirk, Dean Roscoe Pound, Dr. J. R. Sizoo, Professor William E. Hocking, Dr. Robert R. Wicks, Dr. Ralph W. Sockman, Dr. George A. Buttrick, Professor Charles W. Hendel, Professor Kenneth S. Latourette, Mr. Charles P. Taft, Dr. Henry P. Van Dusen, Professor Conyers Read, and by Dr. Theodore Meyer Greene.

PREFACE

I should like to express here my deep personal gratitude to Mr. James W. Rockwell, donor of the Rockwell Lectures, and to President W. V. Houston and his associates at the Rice Institute for the privilege that I enjoyed in delivering the addresses which comprise the present small volume.

As the notable previous Rockwell Lectures demonstrate, it has been customary in this series to deal with topics of general intellectual significance and to consider some of the relationships to social theory and to religion that present themselves in connection with each central theme. My effort, therefore, has been to discuss the making of the modern mind from a biological and psychological point of view but to do this in a way which reflects on some aspects of the political, economic, and social theories of our day. Necessarily also certain questions often considered by theologians have been mentioned.

It would be rewarding, indeed, if some auditor or reader of the lectures were to be stimulated to do further research on some aspects of this extensive field. Out of such work might come a more precise interpretation of what are now in some measure uncomfortably broad generalizations. Scholars today sometimes write as if atomic physics were the only really fundamental scientific study. It may be remembered that modern physics and every other scientific and intellectual endeavor of man depend upon human mental processes and the brain that makes these processes possible. This suggests that the scientific study of the nature and growth of the mind, and especially of inborn biological potentials and limitations of mental processes, is in its own way as basic and fundamental as any other possible topic of human investigation.

Few individual research workers are named in these lectures, and thus credit has not been given to the hundreds of individuals upon whose scientific and scholarly work its pages are based. In this connection it may also be noted that no general bibliography is appended to the book. Those who wish to study in greater detail many of the matters presented here will find rather extensive lists of research papers and general references in the Second Edition of the *Manual of Child Psychology*, edited by me and published in 1954 in New York by John Wiley & Sons.

LEONARD CARMICHAEL

The Smithsonian Institution
Washington, D. C.

I

THE EMERGENCE OF MIND IN THE
ANIMAL SERIES

Few will doubt that there was a time in the history of our globe when there were no human minds. We may well ask, therefore, How was mind first created, or how did mind arise out of non-mind? It is also pertinent to inquire when and how this cosmically important event took place. These related problems have been faced before, but it may not be inappropriate to consider them again, because there is recent scientific evidence that may help us to find some new and more meaningful answers to them.

In the two lectures of the present series I shall deal first with the emergence of mind in the animal series and second with the way in which mind develops as each individual grows from conception to old age.

Formal religion has furnished one answer to the question of the origin or creation of mind, and we may well consider it first. In most of the world's faiths there are stories of creation. The one that has had the most influence on our modern western culture is, of course, that of our Bible. In the Book of Genesis in the King James version, we read, "And the Lord God formed man of the dust of the ground, and breathed into his nostrils the breath of life; and man became a living soul." Again, in the first chapter of the Gospel according to St. John, it is written, "In the beginning was the Word, and the Word was with God, and the Word was God." These Biblical statements are today accepted by many people and may indeed, when fully understood, ultimately be taken as a basis for a final answer to the question of the beginning of mind.

In this paper, however, it is not a religious view but rather various biological and psychological facts and theories about the origin of human mental ability which will be examined. It should not be forgotten, however, that when these two approaches—that of religion and that of science—are fully comprehended they may be found to be supplemental to each other and not in conflict.

The natural origin of the various structures and functions of living species is a difficult and, in our day, not a too fashionable area of biological study and speculation. Laboratory experimentation and controlled observation have shown themselves to be the most fruitful methods for developing scientific truths. Only in very special and limited ways can evolution, as an historic or cosmic process, be subjected to experimental study. The paleontologist, for example, finds in the earth's crust fossil plants and animals. By elaborate, but always indirect, methods he pieces together facts which provide as coherent as possible an account of the successions of these forms that once lived on the earth. He studies skeletal remains in relation to geological strata that have otherwise been dated. A knowledge of the regular rate of conversion of uranium into lead has been used in dating some early remains. Now by the careful measurement of radiocarbon he can assess in a new way the probable age of once-living materials that are not very old. But all this does not say anything directly about the *how* and *why* of evolution. It describes, at best, a time sequence.

In spite of the scientific elegance of much of this paleontological work, speculation and inference have a large share in many of its generalizations. For this and other reasons, during the present century many of those interested in the development of organic types have turned from surmises about the evolution of plants and animals in ages past to a direct present-day study of the growth of individuals as worked out in the science of embryology. Thus the investigator can learn not about an assumed succession of stages in the animal or plant series in the remote past but rather about observable stages in the growth or evolution of present-day individuals. This study is now conducted for its own sake and not mainly in the service of Haeckel's so-called "biogenetic law," which assumed that the life history of each individual is a résumé of the life history of its ancestors. Carleton S. Coon's excellent popular book on anthropology published last year shows that this older view of early structural development is not without its fully proper but still limited importance for students of primitive man, for he says in assessing certain embryological similarities in man and the higher apes that "we know that all animals repeat during embryonic life the general history of their ancestors....".

In that branch of embryology called developmental mechanics growth processes themselves are studied. It is true that all the exact determiners of organic development still are not fully understood, but much concrete scientific information about the chemical and physical factors that underlie the anatomical changes of the maturing individual has been amassed during the past half century. All of this scientific information is important for one who is interested in the growth of the brain and the part that various types of brains play in different mental reactions, but the study of the growth of structures does not deal directly with the development of mind.

It is also important to remember that only in recent decades has genetics, or the study of organic inheritance, become a quantitative science. In this field of investigation, by the use of various experimental techniques, changes in adult forms have been brought about by selective breeding, by the irradiation of the germ cells by X-rays, and in other ways. Thus in our day much of the old speculative Darwinian work upon racial evolution has given place to concrete and specific studies of the relationship between genetic units or genes and embryonic structures as well as with adult characteristics. But this new scientific point of view has been hard

[4]

to apply to developmental psychology. In considering genetics and mental reactions one must ordinarily think of the inheritance of structures and then consider how a changing environment acts on such largely inborn structures rather than try to examine the hereditary transmission of "pure mental functions" of any sort.

These new techniques of embryology and genetics, especially as used together, present special difficulties, therefore, when applied to the origin and development of the processes that in sum make up mind. If one wishes to trace the evolution of the adult human eye muscles or ear bones in their relation to ancestral forms or to embryonic structures one starts with a concrete knowledge of what the rectus superior muscle or the stapes bone is like in the adult. Unfortunately, today, informed scientists are not equally well able to point to a single entity, even so far as function is concerned, when they say they are seeking for the origin of mind. Carbon-14 cannot date the daydreams of our ancestors who first cut ideographs in stone. Nevertheless, the evolution of the brain and other parts of the body that are related to adaptive behavior and to mental life and the role of heredity in creating these structures and functions in each individual must be recognized as fundamental by one who is interested in the growth of the mind in the animal series.

Before we consider the difficult problem of the change from the simplest animal mental processes to those of man, it will be useful to define in some little detail the meaning of two of the words used in the title of these lectures.

The first of these is the word "mind" itself. This word is one of those nouns which, as Londoners remark, the man on the top of the bus understands more surely than does the expert. Everyone thinks he knows what is meant when it is said, "The chap has a keen mind," or "The unfortunate fellow seems to have lost his mind." A scientific definition of mind, however, is not now and never has been easy.

Theologians, philosophers, psychiatrists, anthropologists, and literary men, as well as professional psychologists use this word in many ways that are not identical or sometimes, it seems, even related. In this paper the word mind will be used as a collective noun to include all processes which are now commonly recognized as mental. These activities are called by such names as sensation, perception, learning, motivation, emotion, imagination, reasoning, intelligence, and the like.

Scientific psychological investigations during the last half century have quite well established the fact that all these mental reactions are related to facts and events arising out of the interaction between a living creature and its environment by means of that individual's sense organs, nervous system, muscles, and glands. Mental processes are thus seen to include or be related to activities inside an organism that are typically set off by forces outside of it. The living cells of the body derive their energy until the time of birth from the blood stream of the mother. After that they store up energy which comes from food. When appropriate external energies act on sense organs, these physical or chemical stimuli may trigger, as it were, activities which start other activities which depend on the progressive release of energy stored in nerve, muscle, or other body cells. The nature of these internal activities is thus dependent on the character, pattern, and time relations of stimuli external to the sense organs and upon the make-up, for example, of the brain cells that are energized by changes that can be traced back to sense organ stimulation. Sometimes alterations in the internal environment or in the life processes of the cells themselves initiate activities of the sort just described.

These activities are not always the same. The mental reactions of one who is asleep differ from those of one who is awake. In fact it is rare for the sum total of mental life to be the same for more than a few seconds. Mind as a summarizing name may thus be compared to the word tree. It is easier to say how a tree is related to the rest of nature than to name any parts that are common at all times to all living and growing trees. Mental life cannot be thought of as appearing in complete form at one time in the evolution of the animal series or in the growth of the individual. Mind in this inclusive sense is never erupted fully made like a second eyetooth.

Ever since the time of William James the part played

in the complex set of processes that are called mental in man by so-called consciousness or conscious experience has increasingly been seen to be sharply limited. The definition given above, however, is not intended in any way to exclude conscious phenomena or, indeed, non-conscious or so-called unconscious processes insofar as the facts named by these words are known or can, by direct or indirect means, be made a subject of study or of valid communication from one individual to another.

Certainly, however, an inclusive modern delimitation of the word mind cannot be so narrowed as to deal only with the phenomena of consciousness. When we seek for answers about the origin and development of mind we must study processes and functions which are much more complex than is the emergence of the capacity to be sentient or have what most of us call our conscious experiences.

In the history of the study of the nature of mind this conclusion has not always been clear. Many thinkers in the past who have tried to answer the question of the origin of mental life have assumed that mind is con-sciousness and, therefore, that only conscious phenomena are properly called mental. Some have then taken a further step and asserted that all matter or even all nature is itself psychical or conscious or at least has a psychical aspect. The theory called panpsychism elabo-rated by Gustav T. Fechner and others is a system that makes this assumption. If this view were fully satisfactory there would be no need to speculate about the origin of mind, since it asserts that mind has existed as long as there has also been "matter" or "energy." Panpsychism alleges that conscious experience becomes more and more complex as nerve centers evolve. Fechner contended that in the lower arthropods, which have a chain of ganglia as a central nervous system, there must also be a series of "consciousnesses" related to each ganglia. This would mean that even the great extinct lizards, such as the dinosaurs, would have had mental processes at the level of their hips and shoulders, for the central ganglia at these regions in such animals were comparable in size to their brains.

Today the formal view of panpsychism has few adherents because it is essentially non-factual. No method has been suggested to test its assertions by the ordinary procedures of science.

The older speculative philosophical theories of the relationship between body and mind often tacitly equated mind and consciousness. But to do this now, as has just been pointed out, is to neglect all that has been learned or postulated by physiologists about adaptive behavior and by psychiatrists and psychologists about mental reactions that are, as the now popular phrase has it, more or less deeply nonconscious or unconscious. Epiphenomenalism and psychophysical parallelism are names for two of the varied theories that have been developed and argued about for years by theoretical philosophers. These are descriptive names for schemes developed to account for the apparent relationship between brain action and conscious experience. The first of these theories assumes that consciousness dances along, as it were, with some brain activity but does not influence it. Psychophysical parallelism suggests that nerve action and conscious processes are related in time but do not influence each other. But if the more inclusive definition of mind given above is accepted, all such simple formulations seem quaint and essentially irrelevant to the modern statement of the brain-mind problem. Today many scientists deal with a single psychobiological organism that has a host of processes which are considered in biochemistry and in a number of other specialized sciences, including psychiatry's attempts to consider the deepest human motives that are even sometimes unknown to the individuals who possess them. I have elsewhere tried to write about some aspects of the nature of mind in a more technical way for my psychological colleagues. It will be clear to these friends that what I here call mind, to use older technical words, includes both process and content as well as much that is fully nonconscious.

We may return then to see how the lively, involved, but often quite unified complex of processes which in sum today we see as making up what we have called man's mind or mental life can have started and how these processes developed in the animal series.

[10]

Before we do this we may attempt to tame one more word in our title. This word is "emergence." Much has been written about this concept. Names such as the "doctrine of levels" and "creative synthesis" have been applied to the idea that as processes evolve new totalities are created which are not merely additive but which have properties that were not in any way in the elements that constitute the new whole. A failure to recognize the fact that novel properties typically characterize all really new wholes or new totalities is called the *error of potentiality*. This error, which the distinguished philosopher F. A. Lange has said is the source of most of the world's worst metaphysical fallacies, is a name for the mistake of assuming because certain antecedent events or properties are necessary in order to have a known subsequent event or property that the full physical or other characteristics of the later new totality are somehow latent or hidden in the former more simple elements. Oxygen and hydrogen individually do not necessarily have the hidden characteristic of wetness because water is made up of these two gases. As C. Lloyd Morgan has well said, "The advocate of emergence ventures on the hypothesis: *not there, till it comes*."

No one has better dealt with the error of failing to understand what real emergence is than that sturdy eighteenth-century thinker Bernard de Mandeville, who wrote in his *Fable of the Bees*, "Every grape contains a small quantity of juice, and when great heaps of them

are squeez'd together, they yield a liquor, which by skill-
ful management may be made into wine: But if we consider, how necessary fermentation is to the vinosity of
the liquor, I mean, how essential it is to its being wine;
it will be evident to us, that without great impropriety
of speech, it cannot be said, that in every grape there is
wine."

Thus, in discussing the origin and growth, that is, the
emergence, of human mental processes, I have no wish
to be understood as claiming that at any point the full
wine of the adult human mind with all its subtle and involved processes is somehow to be found lodged in the
grape of any simple reflex twitch, or misty precon-
sciousness, or other early form of behavior or experience
as these processes may be described in the individual or
in the race. Rather, the aim of this lecture is to hold up
and look at a few typical levels in the continuum of the
growth of behavior in the evolutionary series, and then
to consider whether one may think of these stages as the
regular and essential antecedents of the later mental
processes that we know in the minds of real adult
civilized human individuals of today. One who wishes
to think of emergent evolution does not so much try to
explain how the new is created as he does to point to the
great fact of constructiveness in nature and especially in
the biological world.

With this caution or partial explication of the meaning
of the word mind and the word emergence, let us turn

to our central question and look at the growth or gradual unfolding or, in a sense, the ever new creation of mind at various levels of organic complexity in the animal series. For centuries logicians have argued whether the chicken or the egg came first. In this lecture we shall start with the chicken, that is, with racial rather than with individual evolution. The hatching egg will have its turn in the next lecture.

Under one old definition of mind as "the sum of introspectively known conscious events" the question of the study of mental life in the animals below man was difficult and was indeed considered by not a few psychologists as impossible. Margaret F. Washburn, one of America's most distinguished early comparative psychologists, discussed this problem at length. She came to use the term "indirect introspection" to describe the psychologist's act of attributing specific conscious processes to animals other than man on the basis of the behavior they displayed and the type of brain or response mechanism they possessed.

When the broad description of mind given above is used, there is little doubt that man has no monopoly on true mental traits. The great philosopher and mathematician Descartes was wrong when he taught that animals were automata or inanimate machines and that only man had mind. We should not be too hard on Descartes, however, for, as we have already hinted and as we shall say more explicitly at a later point in this lecture, from one point of view man's mind has emerged so as to have characteristics that are unique.

Dog and cat lovers, animal trainers in circuses, and experimental psychologists all know that animals can learn to solve complex problems and in other ways display intelligent behavior. Certain insects organize and maintain elaborate societies in varying external situations. Birds may learn to count and to repeat elaborate patterns of song and speech. All these phenomena and many others have led psychologists to take fundamental interest in the full mental lives of infrahuman organisms. This interest is justified in its own right, but it also has great value in providing keys to unlock many of the otherwise apparently inscrutable secrets of the history of specific human mental processes.

This whole scientific investigation of animal behavior is often well called comparative psychology. Much has been discovered in the study of instinct, learning, perception, motivation, social communication, and other mental processes in animals that do not use language. In adult human individuals the possession of language skills and the ability to use general concepts and to employ the operations of mathematics often so complicate externally observable response that they make determination of the basic characteristics of behavior most difficult to untangle. It may be pointed out, however, that the findings of psychological experiments on infrahuman animals should be applied to man only with caution. Man's mental life is in certain respects unique. This is nowhere better shown than in its effects, good and bad, upon the external world. These effects, which sometimes in fact move mountains, have no parallel in nonhuman creation.

The description and classification of living animals as they are compared one with another constitute a well-recognized subscience of zoology. The Smithsonian Institution estimates that there are over a million different living animal species. Besides the species that are now alive, there are also countless extinct animal forms whose structure is known from the study of fossils. Any reference here to the growth of mental processes as related to the structure of animals in the total evolutionary series must, therefore, at best be schematic and most fragmentary. The study of fossil animal skulls in order to determine the size and nature of extinct animals' brains and, by inference, therefore, something of their behavioral traits has been so developed that today it is a recognized subspecialty in the science of paleontology. Even this work, however, does not give us a basis for a sound fossil psychology.

Logically, indeed, a consideration of the evolution of mind must begin long before skulls or brains appeared. Books and special research papers have been written on the behavior and even on the so-called mind of bacteria or of unicellular organisms such as amoebae. A typical amoeba, as many remember from elementary laboratory work in biology, is a microscopic unit of jellylike proto-plasm living in water. Careful study of these organisms has shown much about the way in which they capture food, move, reproduce, and respond to various forces in the environment in which they exist. From the stand-point of the origin of mind, the startling thing about amoebae is the fact that these single living cells respond differentially and adaptively to light, to vibrations of the sort that make up sound, to chemicals of the kind that in higher animals are the stimuli for taste and smell, and to touch. These tiny featureless organisms in a crude way react to the same environmental forces that impinge upon us, as human individuals, and determine much of our relationship to our own complex and ever-changing environment. Like us, their responses are not just a function of present external stimuli, for their behavior changes when they have or have not recently absorbed food just as our behavior differs when we are hungry or satiated. Some plants such as the so-called Venus flytrap also move quite quickly in response to environmental changes. Strange as it may seem, therefore, papers have been written on the psychology of plants.

The story of the growth of adaptive mental reactions in the animal series is best thought of, however, in connection with the growth or emergence of structures in more and more complex animals which allows the complete organisms to react with increasing effective-ness to the world in which they, as it were, maintain themselves or make their livings. After amoebae, in which a single cell does everything of which the organism is capable, without much specialization of function, one first step forward is seen in certain marine sponges. In these animals, some cells are particularized for the purpose of response. These may be thought of as primitive muscle cells. This is as we should expect it to be, for in all higher animals and even in man physiologists and psychologists know that the brain's basic function, out of which all else has emerged, is, as the great English neurologist Sir Charles Sherrington used to say, *the management of muscle*. It is not too extreme to suggest that when a student begins to think of the brain as directing muscles and not as secreting thought that he has begun to understand the riddle of what the mind of even the sphinx undoubtedly was like.

A next step in the evolution of response is the development of a specialized "connector" or nervous system. The earliest nerve cells were so formed that when the organism possessing them was stimulated at any one place nerve signals spread to all other parts of its body. These nerve nets acted much as would a telephone system with many subscribers but no central office. The next great step forward was the interposition between sense organ and muscle of an integrating, switching, and muscle-controlling system called a ganglion or brain.

Earthworms are good examples of comparatively

simply organisms possessing such a central nervous system. It has been demonstrated, it is true, that the behavior of organisms not having central nervous systems may be modified in certain respects as a result of previous activity. In general, however, organisms without ganglia or brains do not rapidly learn by experience to respond in an effective way to some special part or aspect of the environment as a sign or signal of a previously experienced more complex situation. Worms, however, have been taught such specific habits in the laboratory. The ability to have this sort of behavior modification or learning is all important in the evolution of mind. Somehow in higher organisms changes take place in the chemical and physical make-up of connecting neurons of the central nervous system as a result of previous activity so that their structures are changed. These alterations are such that the behavior initiated by a given external situation is different after previous activity or learning than it was before the habit-forming action had been carried out. In some still unknown way changes of this sort underlie all human memory as well as the learning of worms. The evolution or emergence of this still not too well understood property in certain nerve cells is basic in the growth of the mind. Many of the unchanging characteristics of human nature that are determined by inheritance are related to the specific characteristics and relationships of the cells which make human memory possible. It is especially interesting to note that these living cells, which modern investigations with radioactive tracers have shown to be always changing and largely replaced every few months, still amazingly maintain themselves so that the physical alterations basic to habit and memory persist for years. When an electrical engineer next tells you that a new electronic brain is as good as the brain of man, ask him when he expects to make a tube that will renew the metal of which it is made and not lose the specific "memory" change which it holds as a result of some specific past impulse.

As I have suggested, one of the insistent problems in an attempt to understand the emergence of the real human mind is to determine how much of the behavior of man or of any other species is dependent on heredity and how much on environment. To put this another way, how much of behavior is dependent on the inborn make-up of neurons themselves and of neuron patterns in the central nervous system and how much on the reorganization of this system and its elements as a result of specific reactions and learning during individual life?

A favorite exemplification of why the difference is important is found in a comparison of human and ant social systems. The capacities to form societies by groups of ants and by groups of men are both dependent upon the functioning of the central nervous system. Recent studies have shown that it is possible to alter the social behavior of ants by removing microscopic parts of their inborn central nervous systems. Ant societies are much more dependent upon innate or inborn "wiring diagrams," if we may use this term for the neural structures which determine behavior, than are mammalian and especially, of course, human societies. Of the fifty or more genera of fossil ants preserved in amber, some may be sixty million years old. Some of these genera still persist, and there can be little doubt that the social life of these old family and aristocratic ants was essentially the same when the species was first evolved as it is today. How different this is in the case of much more parvenu human society! For example, some generations of primitive men may well have learned from their parents to act upon now forgotten beliefs in a special kind of magic world that would make some if not all of their social reactions quite unintelligible to most of us today. This is true even though we are separated from them not by millions but only by a few hundreds of generations and because the strange behavior was culturally determined or learned and not inborn as in the ants.

Levels of organization are not the only difference between human and infrahuman societies. Some ant social behavior is complex. In certain tree ants a fertilized female goes out from the colony to establish a new home. She then does things she has never seen done. She chews a bit of bark and makes a tiny nest, often in the middle of a leaf. When the eggs that she lays hatch and develop, workers begin to be active. More and more bark is chewed off. The nest grows. Finally it may be five or six inches in length. The notable thing is that this strange nest, or indeed hundreds of other describable nests, always have a particular character. It may be recognized at a distance as showing that one kind of ant is present. Somehow the inborn connections of the central nervous sytem of these tiny insects are so organized that in somewhat dissimilar external environments similar total, and only to a slight degree varying, nests are built. In one sense we can say that here we see ancestral mind at work, and it is a mind that has remained constant for millions of generations.

Konrad Lorenz has been able to show in his recent studies of bird behavior, such as that of mating, that inborn patterns of response may be a better guide to family relationships in birds than are feather color patterns or even the comparative anatomy of bones. Ornithologists also often can name a bird species as well by looking at its nest as by looking at the bird. In some ways each nest is as much a result of specific chromosomes as is the shape of a leg bone or a bill, but in its development nest building depends on the growth of inborn structures that make possible what may be called ancestral mind. Fishes, reptiles, and birds all are at times influenced in their behavior by others of the same species, but their social and nonsocial reactions are essentially patterned in a way that is characteristic for each group. Students of animal behavior such as Frank A. Beach have shown how the secretions of certain endocrine glands and the growth of specific neural patterns all relate to nest building, reproductive behavior, and other so-called inborn instincts of animals.

The question of the part that glandular secretions and maturing neural and muscular mechanisms, independent of learning and social direction, play in human behavior has long been an active area of debate in psychology. Many students have concluded with a sort of defeatism that heredity and environment are so complexly entwined at each stage in the forming of man's adult mind that it is not profitable even to try to untangle the two strands. But here the student is faced by a paradox. It may be hard or impossible to prove exactly how inheritance works in the making of many aspects of the human mind, for inborn influences can ordinarily be seen only through actions and mental processes that are in part learned. In spite of this fact the question is so important and full of practical implications for economists, political scientists, and philosophers that it has not and cannot be banished from scientific consideration. Today it seems to me that solid evidence from many sides is building up which indicates that in the last generations psychologists and sociologists have underestimated the importance of heredity in the making of human mental life and that this misinterpretation has led to some grave mistakes in man's effort to deal with society on a rational basis.

It may be pointed out that in the great political struggle of our time between communism and the free world a recognition of the part played by inheritance in the making of the structure basic to the human mind has had a real place. The philosophy of communism and of utopian socialism is based upon the unverified and, at its base, essentially mystic assumption of such writers as Rousseau that the so-called natural man is all sweetness and light. These systems assert without scientific evidence that man's social motives are always good and that human nature never shows itself in acts that may be called cruel or selfish except as it is corrupted by a bad society. One reason that a properly understood political conservatism is making so much progress among thinking people today is that philosophers and political scientists who defend the conservative view have always been more willing than their opponents to face the fact that human nature is limited and in some respects essentially unchanging, at least through many centuries of time. These students recognize that at birth man is neither all good nor all bad and that even in adult life, since some aspects of his mind are always limited by the way his neurons are made and by many other facts of his ancestral inheritance, he cannot be made over in one or two generations of changed social living. The conservative thus sees beneath a superficial learned veneer characteristics in human nature and especially in the motives of men that are as old and as unchangeable as is upright posture. Thus, as Russell Kirk has recently pointed out, political conservatives down through the years have tried to deal with men as they are, and not as the wishful thinking of reformers might like them to be.

Therefore, those who are interested in the origin and development of human society are again beginning to see that a biological and psychological study of heredity as well as of learning and of social influences is necessary if one would understand the making of the modern mind. There is need for much more research in this field. The influence of family status and even of remote ancestry is once more quite properly being considered, as well as is the role of education or the provision of more bathtubs, by some of those who hope to preserve a free society and develop a better and better civilization that will produce human achievements of lasting merit. The political scientist, who tries to find out about man's basic characteristics and then takes him as he is, can face the real problems of society and safeguard real human freedom. The utopian socialist has no recourse but the force of the police state when he finds that people do not, in fact, act as his inadequate theories of a wholly environmentally developed human nature make him wish they did.

But let us now leave this psychopolitical illustration and compare man with a most unpromising mammal. No infrahuman animal has been more thoroughly studied by psychologists than the white rat. Nonpsychologists are sometimes a little scornful at the amount of time and energy devoted by psychologists to what seems to them to be a simple and certainly not especially attractive organism. Actually, the white rat has special advantages as an experimental animal for the study of not a few basic psychological processes.

As a result of years of investigation much about the anatomy of the brain of the rat and the internal secretions of its endocrine glands in relation to its behavior systems are quite well known. Rats may be maintained in the laboratory without trouble. They also can be easily bred. By careful breeding, almost genetically pure strains of white rats have become available. Many such organisms can be obtained which are almost identical from an hereditary point of view. The advantage of studying some aspects of inheritance and of learning in the white rat is, therefore, that dozens or even hundreds of similar organisms of the same age and sex can be used by an experimenter. These animals may then be subjected to differing sorts of constant treatment and records can be made of the way in which not just one rat but many of this type perform. By measurement, data are obtained that can then be subjected to statistical treatment. By using complicated mazes, or by providing experimental boxes containing bars which must be pressed to secure food, and in other ways, the learning process and adaptive behavior of white rats have been accurately investigated.

Two examples of rat behavior may be considered here because of the light they throw on mental evolution. By selecting for breeding purposes "bright" rats, which learn quickly, and "dull" rats, which learn slowly, R. C. Tryon has shown that it is possible to produce two strains of rats, each new generation of which will be born with different learning abilities; that is, members of these two strains are not the same in the number of trials that they will require to master certain types of new learning problems. Later, if these two strains are interbred, offspring will be obtained intermediate in ability to learn problems similar to those on which their parents had been tested. This gives strong evidence in favor of the inborn nature of the all important ability to learn. In other recent studies it has been shown that there is an involved relationship between the rate of habit acquisition and the timing of the food or other rewards given to rats as they learn.

Similar curves have been found also to describe the behavior of pigeons and other organisms as they acquire habits. It has even been suggested by B. F. Skinner that pay schedules for industrial workers may sometime be formulated on the basis of principles of reward which were first discovered in the animal experiments of this sort. He suggests that by positive reinforcement a practical control of behavior in both rats and men may be secured. An unpredictable bonus, even if small in a-mount and given on a variable interval schedule, is effective in sustaining a high level of work. The fact that this is true shows something old and mammalian, as it were, about the processes involved. An oversimplified example may be taken. Many generations of social trial and error produced the feudal system of land tenure. This system had defects but it worked. It has recently been pointed out that Marxist efforts to collectivize agriculture did not correct the minor dissatisfactions with the old system but rather killed the individual motivations of the farmers by a new "intellectual system" which somehow failed to take man as he really is. The old system, it is true, produced annoyances which cumulatively led to unrest, but it also was characterized by intrinsic means for the facilitation of diligent behavior on the part of most farmers. In spite of external punishments and rewards the new collective system did not equally well reinforce those behavioral acts which are necessary to make agriculture successful.

Facts such as these suggest how old and fundamental in human nature are some of the inborn factors which lie behind, as it were, innumerable present-day motivations and actions that we all take for granted in our society as we live our daily lives.

By these comparative studies we see that the understanding of the emergence of purely human mental processes is never easy. Some aspects of mental life which at first might seem almost certainly to be the results of human cultural indoctrination turn out to have inborn aspects. It must be repeated, however, that in their novel emergent form all human mental reactions have a history that involves specific inherited and environmental factors which have both interacted in producing them. To put this in another way, the mind of the modern adult man or woman is as it is first of all because man emerged from a cell that had human chromosomes; secondly, because of the particular chromosomes which the individual has inherited from the germ cells carried by his own human parents; and thirdly, because of the specific environmental situations which he has met during his total prenatal and postnatal life.

Mice, raccoons, cats, dogs, horses, sheep, pigs, monkeys, and many other organisms have been studied by experimental psychologists in an effort to describe the characteristics and growth of mental abilities in the animal series. Comparison of different mammals in intelligence or any other mental characteristics is not easy because the kinds of problems differ which by original nature each species is best equipped to solve. If we use the common word "interest" for the full complex of inborn and acquired motives, it is clear that what interests one species of animal seems unimportant to another. Thus the comparison of problem solving or of habit acquisition in different groups of animals becomes very difficult. Comparative anatomy also is never a sure guide to comparative psychology. Brain weight or brain weight as a proportion of body weight does not show any sure quantitative relationship to behavioral capacity when animals are compared even by the tests which seem most nearly valid in their "interest" for a variety of species. This brief statement could be validated by reference to scores of research papers.

No organisms, however, are more important in this connection to the psychologist than are the higher apes. Modern evolutionary theory does not contend that man is directly descended from any existing species of animal such as the present-day chimpanzee or gorilla. But still the minds of the living great apes, like the anatomy of their bodies, are fascinating to us because they characterize the most human of nonhuman organisms.

The importance of understanding what is meant by the emergence of mind is nowhere better exemplified than in the study of the difference between the mind of the ape and that of a competent modern civilized man. Psychologists and anthropologists have given varying lists of the biological characteristics that were necessary to make it possible to say, "and thus a truly human anthropoid appeared." Almost all agree in listing the following as essential if man is to be man: (1) Good sense organs, (2) a brain capable of forming the connections that make speech and memory possible and the processes basic in prolonged attention and abstract reasoning, and (3) erect posture and free-moving and effective arms and hands, which make tool fabrication and tool use easy.

No one knows exactly when or where organisms with

the fortunate combination of these favorable traits first appeared on the face of the earth. Some anthropologists believe that a number of two-legged species of human ancestors came down from the branches of forest trees possibly about twenty million years ago. Once on the ground the characteristics which led to survival began to change. As a result of the climatic rigors of the ice ages and for other reasons, of the earth-walking half-men only the genus *Homo*, hopefully called "the wise" or "*sapiens*", survived. It has been suggested by some authorities that this final ancestral triumph of our true forebears took place between one hundred thousand and thirty-five thousand years ago. This is, of course, yesterday as ant or crab family history is concerned. Since the time *Homo sapiens* as a distinct and triumphant species evolved, anatomical changes in man have been remarkably slight. There is good reason to believe that man's basic mental powers have similarly not altered a great deal since this early time when the race became biologically fixed. Many present-day human limitations in memory, sensory acuity, fatigability, and hundreds of other measurable attributes that characterize modern man were also almost certainly present when true man first became stabilized in an evolutionary sense. Today's well-selected jet pilot probably has neurons and indeed a total nervous system that works no faster and learns no better than did that of an honor guard in the armies of Hammurabi.

If a nonneurologically trained scientist is shown the preserved brain of a gorilla or chimpanzee and for comparison one of man he might well think that the ape brains were small and not well-developed human brains. Actually, years of detailed scientific study of the microscopic as well as of the external anatomy of brains have shown that there are no structures in human brains that are not also represented in the brains of the chimpanzee and gorilla. Essentially all named brain structures indeed are represented in many less manlike mammals. Physiological and anatomical study of the human brain shows, however, that in it the cortex has been much increased and the frontal lobes have become especially well developed. Man's brain to some extent works as a total organ but it also has some quite well localized functions. For example, it has a specific region which when interfered with leads to disturbance of language. It may be emphasized, however, that there are no new types of cellular elements in human frontal lobes or in human language centers that are not also present in the brains of lower mammals.

Thus, while the difference between the brain of man and the gorilla in complexity of its organization is quantitatively slight, somehow this small difference is really *all*-important. The brain of man must almost certainly be similarly better than that of the assumed common ancestor from which modern apes and modern men are thought to be descended. This means that a slight measurable difference is basic to the greatest qualitative or newly emerged difference in the world.

In other words, the key to what is in some respects the absolute and unique difference between man's mind and that of even the highest ape is found in the fact that the human brain and its related sense organs and muscles have allowed the development of man's ability to read and write, use mathematics, construct complex mechanical devices, and develop the kind of esthetic, ethical, moral, and religious life that is dependent not only upon inborn biological characteristics but also on the cultural traditions that are handed on by what is properly called social heredity. Man's brain and the systems of written symbols that this brain makes possible allow each modern generation if it will, through education, to avoid some of the failures and emulate some of the successes and insights of many generations of its parents.

All that social scientists call culture and all specific human institutions have their origin in and depend on human brains, in the recent or distant past as well as in the present. Man's old brain with its constituent neurons is thus basic to the modern human mind because it allows each child, who is fortunate enough to be able to do so, to profit by some of the accumulated and organized wisdom of the social past.

One may speculate about the possibility that, by some mutation in the germ cells of our early ancestors, brains may have been developed that were ready to use language perhaps thousands of years before speech was invented. A brain capable of directing human speech but not conditioned by a learned language would not in our modern sense be human. Words as well as an organism capable of using words were necessary before mind dawned in the previously nonhuman mental world.

The great apes do not use language in this human way. Studies of the gorilla, the orangutan, and the chimpanzee in the wild state and in captivity bear out this statement. These animals may be noisy, but much that these cousins of ours have to say to us about psychology is important because they do not talk. In the next lecture we shall see that the infant chimpanzee matures more rapidly as a solver of problems and in other mental ways during its first year than does the human baby. R. M. Yerkes, possibly the greatest student of anthropoid behavior in our generation, has said, "The great apes are incomparably more like man socially than is any other existing creature", but still they do not use true language in an advanced way. It is important to remember that chimpanzees, like man, at birth are quite helpless. The perpetuation of this species requires prolonged maternal care as does that of man. In the wild, the chimpanzee father, as well as the mother, contributes to the care of the young. When a high tree is to be climbed or a long branch-to-branch jump to be made, he may temporarily take over the problem of transporting the baby. It has also been observed in the wild, that adults, and especially active preadolescent chimpanzees, participate in playing with the family baby. They bring it twigs and as the baby becomes stronger play games of tag and wrestle with it. Indeed, the study of the play of animals is an interesting small key that has value for one who would try to open some of the doors of the nature of mental evolution.

Much has been discovered about the emergence of complex mental processes by the study of chimpanzee infants. In recent years, Dr. and Mrs. Keith J. Hayes raised a female chimpanzee baby, Viki, in their home. I had an opportunity to watch Viki at different intervals during most of her development. Unfortunately this scientifically important animal recently died of pneumonia. During the years of her life I enjoyed a number of pleasant meals with the Hayes family, including Viki. In spite of painstaking efforts by her foster parents, however, Viki did not develop an effective use of language. Laboriously she learned to say a few words. On the other hand, she developed in the home situation some remarkably human characteristics. She loved to do finger painting. Not a few of her canvases were so excellent that they might have been prize winners in a show of nonobjective artists. If, in paging through a magazine she saw a picture of a watch she might lift the page and try to listen to the tick. She also learned to imitate—for imitation is at least in part learned—in a very human way. When shown any of dozens of photographs of human subjects she would perform the action represented in the pictures. She dressed and undressed at the request of her human step-parents. A reward of candy was given her for success in toilet training. Later she would herself get the candy out of its jar and go to the toilet. If she did not succeed, with sad reluctance but without prompting she would put the candy back in its jar. Here in a single example we see how subtle and sensitive is the boundary between human and non-human mental life. This act of Viki may make us ask if only man has a conscience.

Chimpanzees, like men, are social animals. In his famous book, *The Mentality of Apes*, Wolfgang Köhler points out that a chimpanzee kept in solitude is not a real chimpanzee at all. It has been amply demonstrated at the Yerkes Laboratories of Primate Biology in Florida, the world's greatest chimpanzee research center, that chimpanzees thrive under human as well as chimpanzee companionship, but this close association never makes apes into men or the laboratory scientists into chimpanzees. Controlled laboratory studies of chimpanzees have clearly shown, however, that in appropriate circumstances these animals will cooperate in performing complex tasks that require two or more animals in order to secure a reward such as food. Can this be called a first step in the "social contract" so dear to the theories of some old political scientists? Chimpanzees have also been taught to use poker chips as a sort of primitive money. They learn to hoard coins that are valuable and discard those that cannot be later used in a "chimpo-mat" to secure food or other desired rewards. Can the economist here learn about basic traits that he must consider if his theories are to fit the old mammal that is just below the surface in man?

It has been said that only man uses tools to make tools. Chimpanzees have been observed, however, to use stones as hammers to break other stones and thus make a sharp edge on a second stone, which is then used in scraping. Counting has been demonstrated in the higher apes and in other mammals and, as we have noted, even in birds. The use of true geometric concepts such as triangularity and circularity, not mere triangular and circular shapes, has been demonstrated as determining adaptive behavior in cats and other animals as well as in the infrahuman primates.

All these observations are typical of many findings that indicate that the so-called higher thought processes of man involving abstract symbols, language, the use of numbers, and even conscience or superego are not as exclusively human as proud human beings might wish to think.

It must be emphasized, however, that some of these processes are rudimentary in every organism save man, and even in man, as we shall see in the next lecture, every mental process has specific limitations in adult life and even more restricted boundaries in infancy and child-hood. We see in these examples, therefore, the necessity of recognizing the complexity and subtlety of the processes that have made the emergence of the modern man's mind possible. In old fashioned cartoons, one sometimes saw a dotted line leading from the head of an individual and ending in a closed balloon. In the balloon words were printed which were supposed to represent the thoughts of the individual. The mental processes of all organisms below man can be represented in such closed and limited balloons. The general limits of communication, counting, delay between sense impression and differential muscular action, and the use of abstract concepts by chimpanzees and other animals are now quite well known, at least in outline form, as a result of the work of experimental psychologists. In a state of nature there is little evidence in any animal below man of the cumulative social transmission of the new inventions of one generation to succeeding generations. I know of nothing to suggest that a young adult wild chimpanzee, separated by even a thousand generations from an earlier chimpanzee family, would find any unexpected elements in the pattern of the later family's life. How different is man! Only about three hundred generations have passed since the beginning of agriculture. The making of fire by friction and the ability to shape stones by flaking took place far back in human history. Both of these arts require real skill, as anyone who tries them today can testify. Such skills, when once discovered, are passed down through the generations. During the passage of recent generations, human culture has changed with dazzling rapidity.

It is important for social scientists and would-be reformers of mankind to remember, however, that anatomically during this period man has changed little, if at all. It is not hard to surmise, therefore, that even as biologically conservative an organism as man may prosper best in a relatively stable society in which interpersonal relationships are governed by usages that have been evolved by generations of social trial and error and by the gradually developed patterns of what may be called comfortable living. The old prayer of men to do their duty in that state of life into which it shall please God to call them may sound old fashioned. This prayer, however, may be more basic in suggesting the road to effective adaptation of biologically old human beings to social living than the recent kaleidoscopically changing generations of the West like to realize, especially since the French Revolution and the coming of widespread industrialization.

To return, howerver, to our analogy of the cartoonist and the balloons, we must conclude that the balloon that represents man's mental life is not a closed space like that of the chimpanzee but is open and capable of unlimited expansion. Human minds, in some respects, know no

[38]

fixed limits to their potential intellectual, artistic, or religious development. This means that we can be sure that some aspects of the society in which our great-great-grand-children will live will be as different from ours as our social life is from that of the period of President George Washington. But we can also be sure that in other basic respects this future society will be as similar to ours as ours is to the glittering eighteenth century or indeed to classic times.

The great task of making the sane and achieving modern mind as effective as possible is to find a balance between a biologically conservative organism and a brain in that organism that is capable of profiting by beneficial social change. The Swiss psychiatrist Carl Jung has elaborated a complex system which attempts to deal, in what seems to me to be somewhat involved symbolic terms, with some of the ancient elements in all modern minds. He speaks of a collective or racial unconscious in which the human heritage of the past is somehow still represented in nonconscious processes in each living mind. This is not the time or the place for a full critique of this important and involved psychiatric conception, but it is interesting to note that in this system the same recognition of the conservatism of the human mind that has been emphasized in this biologically based paper is given full recognition, although it is approached from a very different starting point.

Geologists estimate that the earliest known rocks of

our globe are as much as or even more than four billion years old. It is thought that placental animals, that is, mammals that bear their young alive and nurse them, have existed on the earth only for sixty to seventy million years. Organisms with manlike characteristics have probably existed for less than one million years. True human individuals, with a culture and a written symbolism, who could produce a pattern of thought at all comparable to that of the adult human mind of civilized man today may have been in existence for only ten or fifteen thousand years. The minds of modern men, therefore, as we now know them in their present infinite variety and power, must be thought of not only as a unique and novel emergence but also as a very recent phenomenon in the cosmos.

Somehow, in a few millennia this modern human mind has organized systems of ethics and discovered or developed other value systems and learned the ever more and more adequate revelations of religion. The power of this mind is seen in the present advanced state of industry, politics, finance, science, literature, painting, sculpture, architecture, music, and religion. Coherent philosophic systems dealing with the ultimate questions of man's very existence have been evolved by these minds. Human minds through applied science and technology have in a few centuries enlarged man's power over his world and himself and have made it possible for him to improve or spoil a surprisingly large

part of the surface of the globe. Man's mind has invented ways to prevent or cure human diseases. It has
developed the use of fossil fuels and other forms of
energy instead of the puny pulls of mammalian muscle
cells. Man's mind has leveled hills and united oceans.
Surely this mind of modern man, this recently emerged
complex of functions and processes, is awe-inspiring in
its unique power. Some aspects of this mind as we have
seen are older than the mammals, but it is its peculiar
genius that in other respects it is always a synthesizing
novelty. Today mind is in part as modern as is the use of
atomic energy in airplanes because minds living today
have in part made this development possible.

The pattern of the normal adult mental life of the
modern civilized man thus includes all the functions and
processes given in the definition of mind presented at
the start of this paper. As we shall see in the next lecture,
when we consider the growth of mind in the individual,
a typical adult mind cannot be comprehended in terms
of any single cross section of consciousness or of behavior as cut for inspection at any one time. It can only
be understood as its functions and powers are studied
during long periods in each individual life and in the
whole life of the race.

A few words have just been said about the psychiatric
system of Jung. It is also true that much that Freud,
Adler, and other psychoanalysts have contributed to
psychiatry helps us to understand the involved character

of our own and other people's healthy or diseased minds. Because of these insights of psychoanalysis, no one who now tries to understand any specific human mind will ever again neglect the importance of the basic urges and motives of human life. This is true even if some of these deeply important dynamic factors are not always consciously known to the individual himself. In the modern human mind, therefore, the reactions and especially the emotional patterns of response that are acquired by a growing but still, in a sense, old ancestral brain during infancy, childhood, and adult life turn out to be important in understanding the deeper energetics of the normal and also slightly or markedly abnormal traits that we all know or half suspect in others or even in ourselves.

In the next lecture we will turn to consider how this mind characteristically changes in each individual and how, through amazingly complex growth process and by formal and informal habit formation and education the little apes of the human family are gradually transformed into the more or less effective adult members of modern society. In this lecture, from amoeba to man, we have seen something of both the continuity and the discontinuity of development of the incomparable mind of man. In its elements we have noted that nothing in human mental life is wholly new, but in its totality we have seen that the modern human mind is novel, unique, and without a rival in significance and in its awe-inspiring potential power in the full universe of created things.

The next lecture will try to trace the growth of mental life from the first twitch of the fetus to the variety of forms and patterns which it shows in the normal, achieving, adult, modern, civilized man or woman.

II

THE EMERGENCE OF MIND
IN THE GROWING INDIVIDUAL

In the preceding lecture we considered the emergence of the modern adult human mind as the end product of a long history of the growth of mental powers in the animal series. In this lecture we shall discuss the gradual unfolding of mental life as it takes place during the growth of each human individual.

Folklore and prescientific speculation from earliest antiquity have played with the notion that the "quickening," that is, the onset of motility in the human fetus, in some way indicates the beginning or the zero point of each individual human mind. Modern science does not contradict this view, but the reason for this agreement is noteworthy. Anthropologists have shown that primitive men in all cultures have been deeply concerned with the difference between life and nonlife. Human beings, primitive or modern, can never fail to face the hard fact that a living person has many characteristics unlike one that is dead. In the absence of advanced scientific knowledge it seems to be natural for men to see all organic movement and especially all purposeful action as dependent upon an assumed animating principle of some sort. This breath or power is thought of as living with and directing the animal organism but not as being part of its body. Some primitive people are careful not to awaken a sleeping person lest his animating principle be lost because it may be at some other place in a dream. By analogy, the movements and characteristics of the sun, stars, clouds, and nonliving nature generally have also been attributed by early wise men to specific local spirits of some sort. This simple explanation of what makes living and nonliving things move and have their special characters is called primitive animism.

In much more subtle form a comparable modern animism has been elaborated by some philosophers. Bergson and a number of vitalistic biologists have held that in the last analysis a vital force that is superior to and above mere chemical and physical action is needed to explain the behavior of animals and men. The late Willam McDougall, professor of psychology at Harvard, defended one such view in relation to animal and human mental life.

An opposing nonvitalistic conception of animal behavior and of the human mind has had a place in the history of speculative philosophy and biology at least since the time of Lucretius and his classic predecessors. In the early part of the present century, under the influence of objective physiologists such as Bethe and Loeb, the idea of tropistic or mechanistically determined responses of parts of the body or of the total organism itself to environmental stimuli was given elaborate formulation. This point of view and the related idea of the modification of responses through the conditioning of reflexes as emphasized by Pavlov were taken over and applied to psychology by certain students of human nature who called themselves behaviorists. John B. Watson, E. B. Holt, A. P. Weiss, and many other early American objective psychologists were strictly non-vitalistic in their thinking. But it may be emphasized that these objectivists, like primitive or modern animistic thinkers, based their psychological generalizations on the observation and recording of what organisms and living people were observed as doing. These objective scientists described the external conditions under which behavior takes place and the nature of response itself. The vitalists also observed and described behavior but saw in it an expression of an inner and always non-observable principle of some mysterious sort.

It is thus clear that mechanistically or nonmechanistically considered there is nothing novel or unexpected in the study of what an organism does by one who wishes to discover the origin and development of the mental activities of the organism. Today it is also clear that one who would understand behavior must give full consideration to all the factors by means of which normal men become so largely "inner directed." Everyone knows that the adult normal human being is not directed in his actions merely by present sights and sounds but acts as he does in part because of inner processes which are often accompanied by thoughts which are sometimes similar, as we shall see, to silent speech. To make matters more confusing, some of these dynamic factors in human life, although now considered by many as non-vitalistic, are, nevertheless, recognized as nonconscious or unconscious. If we are to explain such processes and not just sidestep them, as it seems to me those who accept animism do, or deny them, as some crude mechanistic philosophers and psychologists do, we must study with care the stages of growth of behavior and related conscious and nonconscious processes in the individual.

In the consideration of the onset of mind in the child it is appropriate, therefore, to begin with a review of the observations that have been made on the behavior of very young human organisms. As explained in the first lecture, this does not mean that we must begin with speculations about the so-called onset of consciousness although, as we have just noted, what are commonly called conscious or indeed unconscious processes in the child and adult are not to be neglected when they emerge and can be described.

There are references to the prenatal development of behavior in relation to the growth of mind in ancient Egyptian, Hebrew, and Chinese writings. In pre-Socratic Greek antiquity it was held that the general form of the body is completed in males many days before it is similarly finished in females. This discriminatory embryological notion (no doubt written by men) persisted for many centuries. Even in early Christian canon law the moment of animation and of the entrance of the soul was recognized as the fortieth day after insemination for males and the eightieth day for females.

By the time of Aristotle the bodily life and the animating principle, or the mind, of the unborn child began to be considered in some detail. In the third chapter of Aristotle's great treatise on embryology, the entrance of the various souls into the embryo is discussed. In transmuted form these ideas appear in both patristic and scholastic philosophy. Aristotle explicitly taught that the vegetative or nutritive soul, or general animating principle, existed in the unfertilized material of the embryo. In regard to this point he says:

> "...for nobody...would put down the unfertilised embryo as soulless or in every sense bereft of life (since both the semen and the embryo of an animal have every bit as much life as a plant).... As it develops it also acquires the sensitive soul in virtue of which an animal is an animal.... For first of all such embryos seem to live the life of a plant, and it is clear that we must be guided by this in speaking of the sensitive and the rational soul. For all three kinds of soul, not only the nutritive, must be possessed potentially before they are possessed actually."

One of the writers of the patristic period, Tertullian, held that the soul was fully present in the embryo throughout uterine life, but St. Thomas Aquinas taught that the soul entered the fetus in the second gestation month and sex in the fourth. More completely, it was the view of St. Thomas that the fetus was first endowed with a vegetative soul, which in due course perished to be immediately supplanted by the rational soul. This view, as is so often the case in writings of the Angelic Doctor, can, if its obvious quaintness of terminology is brushed aside, still today be defended at least in a symbolic way. Dante also, with surprising insight, says, "So soon as in the fetus, the articulation of the brain is perfect, the primal motor turns to it with joy over such an art of nature...and makes one single soul which lives and feels...."

In an illustration in a manuscript of St. Hildegarde of Bingen, probably made about A.D. 1150, the descent of the soul into the unborn embryo is shown. Here we see angels pouring in good gifts to the future human being through a sort of celestial umbilical cord; but we also, I regret to say, see a little black devil pouring in his gifts of evil. This has a symbolic significance of importance for us today. It suggests facts, as noted in the previous lecture, that are too often neglected by mistaken modern Communists, Socialists, and other utopian dreamers. These theorists about human nature (for that is what they are) pretend to believe that people can be transformed just by changing their housing or their social security policies, without remembering the symbolic little black devil of St. Hildegarde's picture. Men have inborn natures that are in part as old and conservative as the mammals, and, therefore, any exclusively environmentalist view of mind and the idea that human society can be made perfect just by providing more machines or other purely external improvements seems doomed to failure. This extreme environmentalist view of the origin of mind arises to haunt us today in a dangerous way because it is in essence the basic mistake that is at the root of some of the worst errors of the action programs of utopian socialism and Marxist communism.

These would-be reformers are at once antibiological and antireligious as they try to convince themselves that men need not make an effort to be good or personally try to resist what theologians have long called sin, but that a changed environment will make all people perfect in one or two generations. When this transformation does not work, because it is based on a mistaken view of human nature, the reformers, if they love power as do most men, can have recourse only to a police state. A revolver at the temple thus becomes the substitute that disillusioned utopians resort to when they abandon training individuals by age-old and tested methods of social and religious reinforcement to be inner directed, self-controlled, and anxious to be as ethically good as they can be.

But we must return to our story, for St. Hildegarde's picture has led us ahead in our consideration of the growth of adaptive behavior in very young human beings.

Modern scientific thinking about the growth of individual human mental life goes back, as did prescientific speculation, to the onset of motility in the still unborn child. It is unfortunate, therefore, that it is not easy to state dogmatically exactly when the first bodily movement that is relevant to later mental life begins in the normal developing human fetus. This first real quickening, whenever it takes place, may well be considered as the best starting point in the study of mind that we are likely to find in the long process of individual human mental development. The reason that it is difficult to say exactly when the first response occurs is that, as is true with almost everything in biology, as soon as any phenomenon has been isolated and described it at once becomes clear that this process itself is inseparably linked with one that was going on before it began. Biological events, in other words, generally evolve rather than begin *de novo*. Here again we see the importance of a clear understanding of the meaning of the concept of emergence which was discussed at some length in the preceding lecture.

In considering the onset of human motility, the question may be asked as to whether fetal heartbeat is a true response of the total organism. The heartbeat begins in the fetus at about the third week after insemination, that is, in an organism that is still less than one-eighth of an inch in length. This early heartbeat is essentially an automatic muscle response. At first it is not a neurally induced or controlled activity. Heartbeat in its early form, therefore, is not generally considered as the starting point of truly adaptive responses which always involve sense organs, nervous system, and muscles. As structural growth continues, however, the sense receptors, nervous system, and muscles develop, and at length external physical stimulation can lead to movements of the trunk and of the limbs. When this first becomes possible we have come to the start of adaptive behavior and hence at the onset of processes that are basic to what we shall later call mental life. It is especially important, therefore, to consider the way in which the various parts of this system gradually become functional during the months after conception and before birth.

With the awakening of sensory function each receptor field comes to play a special part in the determination of behavior in the fetus and later in the action and experience of the newborn and adult individual. In the one hundred and fifteenth Psalm, what is said of idols might well be applied to the fetus at the stage before such function begins:

"They have mouths, but they speak not: eyes have they, but they see not:
They have ears, but they hear not: noses have they, but they smell not:
They have hands, but they handle not: feet have they,

but they walk not: neither speak they through their throat."

In the fetus, thus, like the famous metaphorical statue of the philosopher Condillac which became more and more human as one by one functional senses were added to it, we may trace the development of early active life in connection with the growth of its senses as well as with its maturing nervous system and muscles.

At birth the young organism faces a host of new stimuli. Strangely enough, however, newborn mammals differ very much in their capacities at this crucial time. The opossum is born thirteen days after insemination as essentially an early fetus, except that it can breath, move its legs well enough to transport itself by its own efforts to the maternal pouch, and then take nourishment through its mouth. The guinea pig, on the other hand, is born more than sixty days after insemination and at birth has its eyes open, its fur coat developed, and is in many respects an adult organism. The human infant at birth is in some ways midway between these two in functional development. It is indeed helpless, for although its senses and muscles are ready to function they are not yet strong. Many of the human responses present at birth, although elicited by new stimuli, after leaving the mother's body, merely call into play sensory-neuromuscular mechanisms that have long been functional in fetal life. This is demonstrated by the fact that many of the responses of the normal new-born infant can be called out by proper stimuli in premature infants who have sometimes had many weeks less than a full term of fetal growth.

A comparison of human and animal infants has much to tell the psychologist about the basic motives of life. I have recently seen a newborn giraffe, after a gestation period of over four hundred days, lie quivering and inert with the ruptured amniotic sac about it like a blanket. In less than twenty minutes after birth this animal struggled hard to get to its feet but failed. It then seemed to try harder still, got to its feet, and held its head erect, more than five feet high. It moved directly to the mother and without error found the maternal nipples and nursed long and successfully, moving from nipple to nipple. Here there was no opportunity for learning, and thus it seemed to me that I was watching innate mammalian behavior and motivation as it emerged with utmost clarity. At an early period in my academic life I would hardly have believed the observation that I have just recorded because I was then so much under the influence of the idea that all adaptive behavior had to be learned by trial and error by each individual.

In certain later research papers, however, I have shown, on the basis of experimental evidence, that the anticipatory maturation or development of structures before the time when such functions are ordinarily necessary to preserve life may be called out by proper stimulation. This is often true before learning begins. This I have called the law of anticipatory function. It is of general importance in considering the elaboration of structure and function in the early stages of growth of the organism.

Studies of human fetuses delivered by operation in order to preserve the life of the mother have demonstrated that the earliest functioning of sense organ, nerve, and muscle connections appears at approximately the eighth week after fertilization. If at this time the skin of the face of the human fetus is stimulated by a standardized hair—a so-called aesthesiometer—the head may be seen to turn away from the stimulus. Davenport Hooker and other investigators have shown that at this time the arms may move down and the trunk be partially rotated as the body arches away from the point that has been touched. Movements that are similar to these are sometimes seen in fetuses of about this age even though no external pressure or other type of stimulation has been directly applied. Movements of this latter sort are called spontaneous, although they probably result from internal stimulation of the central nervous system brought about by changes in the blood.

During fetal life and indeed during all later life the condition of the internal environment, that is, the chemical make-up of the blood and body fluids, is most important as a basis for normal brain action. More than a century ago a great French physiologist, Claud Bernard, demonstrated that the constancy of the internal environment is the condition of the free life. The maintenance of this constant or steady state by regulators in the body itself or homeostasis, as it has been termed, is essential to all the processes which are called mental at all stages of life, at least in the higher animals and man. Take an adult man to the top of a high mountain and thus reduce the oxygen in his blood or add alcohol or other drugs to his blood stream and strange mental changes may appear which often disclose basic facts about each individual personality. Recently special drugs have been used to calm excited mental patients and other drugs have been used to attempt to bring out thruthful replies from those who are trying to lie.

During the fourth fetal month additional response mechanisms mature. At this time the entire body surface becomes sensitive to pressure stimulation. By the fifth month, movement becomes so general that the mother is often clearly aware that the unborn child she bears is active. At this time reflex grasping follows stimulations of the palm, and other very specific responses develop.

Human fetuses fourteen to sixteen weeks of age which are removed by operation show swallowing and respiratory movements. All the reactions of the fetus during late fetal life are conditioned by the fact that the cells of the central nervous system develop their adult functions slowly. There is also relative oxygen lack in the blood available to the late fetus.

At the time of normal birth the cerebral cortex has its full complement of cells but has not yet developed anything like its adult capacities. Occasionally children are born without a cerebral cortex. Such children may show normal reflexes for a time because the central nervous system below the cortex is in satisfactory working order. A study of the electrical activity of the brain in normal newborn babies also demonstrates that the cells of the cortex at this time lack the characteristic rhythms that appear later.

The question whether the unborn fetus has consciousness of any sort and, indeed, the question whether the late fetus is even dimly aware of its surroundings have been debated for many years. It seems clear that if the late fetus or the newborn child does have any experience it must be, to use William James's famous phrase, a "blooming, buzzing confusion." In spite of this fact superstitious ideas have arisen suggesting that the mother's thoughts and experiences directly influence and are felt by the unborn fetus. Prenatal influences of this kind, however, have long been recognized as having no serious place in science. It may be interesting to note, however, that the distinguished philosopher Malebranche years ago spoke of the complete sharing of all mental processes between fetus and mother. Even Hegel spoke of the fact that before birth the fetus and mother are in an undivided "psychic unity."

It is suggested that this essentially magic relationship must be of the nature of some nonscientifically known type of animal magnetism by means of which the character and talents of the mother are believed to be directly communicated to the child. Biologically there is, of course, no connection between fetal and maternal organisms except through cell walls in placental blood vessels. There is no direct neural connection between mother and fetus in any mammal. It is amusing to note that, in spite of these long-known facts, even in modern medical literature not a few articles are found pointing out surprising coincidences between maternal mental processes and fetal characteristics. An expectant mother longs for strawberries and cannot, as she says, get them out of her mind. Weeks later her child is born with a strawberry mark on its skin. This is certainly only a coincidence, but still it has such emotional reinforcement that it is hard to convince the mother that her mental processes did not affect her unborn child's epidermis.

Birth is always a dramatic event in each mammalian life. At the time of birth, a new organism, which previously has lived in a protected liquid environment of constant temperature and with a specific gravity very much like its own body, is faced with many new stimuli and novel adjustments. At first after birth the human baby is very weak and wholly unable to act so as to satisfy its needs. It does not show the same adaptive innate behavior that is seen so dramatically in the giraffe and other ungulates; but, as we have seen, this strange newborn human organism not only has an unrivaled mental future but also it already has a considerable behavioral past. Muscles which were able to respond in an adaptive and even graceful way while emersed in the amniotic fluid now are not able to overcome gravity, but soon the slow climb of the human individual to adulthood and relative self-sufficiency begins.

Even at the actual birth time the human being is not wholly placid. One of the phenomena of birth that has long attracted the attention of those interested in the origin and development of mental life is the first cry of the baby. The great philosopher Immanuel Kant made the following, to me most unphilosophical, statement about this initial phonation:

"The outcry that is heard from a child scarcely born has not the tone of lamentation, but of indignation and of aroused wrath; not because anything gives him pain, but because something frets him; presumably because he wants to move, and feels his inability to do it as a fetter that deprives him of his freedom."

That this type of interpretation is not entirely dead can be attested by the fact that not a few psychoanalytically oriented physicians today speak of the birth cry as an expression of the infant's overwhelming sense of inferiority at thus suddenly being confronted by reality without ever before having had to deal with its problems. The psychoanalyst Otto Rank has made much of the "birth trauma" in his system of psychiatric thought. Today many of those who follow the work of this influential writer interpret his suggestions about the individual's feelings and memory of the pains of birth in a symbolic rather than in an actual sense. Scientifically the birth cry itself is known not to be a wholly new phenomenon. Prematurely delivered infants have been heard to cry a number of weeks prior to normal birth time, for the vocal mechanism is one that obeys the law of anticipatory function.

Among the responses that are present at birth in the human baby are opening and closing of the eyes and contraction and dilation of the pupil. Coordination of the eye movements often appears during the first day. True eye convergence develops in the first few days. Tears may be secreted but not in large quantities on the first day. Many facial and throat responses are present at this time, including sucking, crying, and babbling.

The first two weeks of an infant's life after birth are generally referred to as the neonatal stage. After this comes the rather long period of infancy, which is often considered as lasting for the first two years. The period of childhood is then considered to last from the second year until puberty, at which time the period of adolescence is said to begin. Adolescence is in turn more or less terminated—in some fortunate (or should one say unfortunate?) individuals—when the period known as adulthood begins. Then, if ever, we surely have the adult modern human mind, the emergence of which we are seeking in this paper.

Most of the behavioral changes that take place during fetal and neonatal periods may be attributed to the growth and maturation of the living cells of the developing organism. Most important in the maturation of human behavior and mental life, however, is the growth and change of the structures that make response possible, that is, the nervous system and its constituent cells or neurons and the terminal organs related to this system.

At or just before birth a new type of behavioral change, which is not merely the result of growth processes, begins to be apparent in the infant. This new way of altering responses is called *learning*. In some ways learning is similar to growth. Learning, however, can be distinguished from growth, even at this early period, because it can be shown that responses that are learned appear only after specific activity on the part of each organism. In the previous lecture some characteristics of learning as it first appeared and developed in the animal series were considered.

A good many experiments have been carried out in an attempt to answer the question of when real learning can be said to begin in the normal human individual. There is now evidence that very simple learning or conditioning is possible in fetal life. It has also been shown that food-taking reactions can be learned immediately after birth. In one experiment newborn babies were fed six times a day, starting when they were twenty-four hours old. Two to five trials were given at each feeding by taking the bottle away, then giving it back to the baby after a buzzer had been sounded. Soon the experimenter found that at the sound of the buzzer alone the babies made anticipatory feeding movements.

There is much evidence that learning as we know it in adult life is largely dependent on a functional cerebral cortex. The fact that normal newborn babies have a cortex that is far from fully developed is another reason for believing that the abilities to learn and to have so-called "conscious experience" are both minimal at birth in the human organism. All evidence, indeed, seems now to point to the view that not only the physiological capacity to learn, as just indicated, but also by far the most important part of behavioral change during early infancy is still the result of the growth or maturation of those parts of the nervous system that make such functions possible. A great deal of effort is now wisely being devoted in psychology to determine exactly what characteristics of behavioral change in early months and years may be considered as the result of growth and what may be dependent on learning. It is important to remember that growth or what is called maturation continues to be important in bringing about behavioral change long after the organism has developed a brain that makes learning possible. Indeed, if reproductive behavior is included, maturational factors are still significant, although overlaid by much learning at adolescence. Other maturational changes are seen in some of the mental alterations that characterize old age.

Experiments on growth or maturation and on learning have been carried out on animals below man in the evolutionary scale, as we saw in the last lecture. It is possible to control both certain hereditary and environmental factors in such animals in a manner not possible in human beings. Some experiments I performed a good many years ago indicate that organisms can grow and develop normally while under an anesthetic and hence remain immobile as they mature. When the anesthetic is removed and stimuli are allowed to affect such experimentally developed organisms, the previously drugged animals respond about as effectively as do control organisms that were motile and subject to active stimulation as they grew up. This emphasizes the part that inner determined growth rather than external learning plays in behavior development.

The advantages of the higher and distinctly human type of learning do not become apparent during the early part of infancy. Chimpanzee infants and human babies have been reared together and under as nearly identical external conditions as possible. In one such experiment conducted by W. N. Kellogg, a chimpanzee female was brought into the home of the investigator when she was seven and a half months old. At this time she was two months younger than the psychologist's baby with whom she was reared. Both infants were fed, dressed, punished, and kissed in the same way. Both slept in similar beds and had similar playthings. The chimpanzee learned to skip, to cooperate, to kiss for forgiveness, to open doors, to go to the bathroom in advance of bladder and bowel reactions, to eat with a spoon, and to drink from a glass in a manner superior to the child. The chimpanzee during this period was also superior in strength, in ability to localize auditory sounds, and in response to verbal stimuli such as "shake hand" or "bad girl." At the age of twelve months the chimpanzee infant could respond appropriately to twenty such verbalizations. The comparable human child at this time could respond to only three. The investigators say that unquestionably the chimpanzee was able to eat from a spoon, drink from a glass, skip, and announce her bladder and bowel needs in advance better than the average child of her own age because she learned this behavior more rapidly. Gradually at first, and then very quickly, however, slower-starting human children catch up and soon wholly outdistance all animal rivals.

This human superiority may be thought of as due to

the fact that the great cerebral hemispheres of the human infant continue to grow in functional capacity for many months after birth. One obvious result of this development is that greater and greater delay between stimulation and response becomes possible for human children as compared with chimpanzees or any other infrahuman mammals. This capacity for delayed reaction is probably to be thought of as intimately associated with the anatomical maturation of the cerebral hemispheres. The slow but all important growth in the child of the use of language and of other symbolically controlled behavior is related to and, at times, essential in response changes.

There has been much study of the nature of language development in relation to the amount of practice and to the growth of the brain. For example, it has been shown that a given amount of language training at eighty-nine weeks of age is quantitatively much more effective than similar training at eighty-four weeks of age. This and many other isolated bits of evidence seem to make it clear that the reason that language does not develop in early human infancy is because the brain centers basic to language have not grown at that time in such a way as to make the use of words easy. Once the nervous system has developed to the point that real communication by true verbal means can be carried out, the whole course of individual human behavioral change is modified. Language is so interwoven with other aspects of human behavior that twins living together but reared somewhat apart from adult stimulation often elaborate and use quite effectively languages which are in some part their own inventions. Biological readiness, as all teachers know, is essential for efficient learning of such subjects as reading and arithmetic. Before the brain is fully ready to learn these subjects, practicing them is to some extent wasted effort.

Most of the real words that children learn in any society are to be thought of as inherited from the linguistic past of the social group into which they are developing. This is true even of so subtle a thing as regional accent. Each word that the child learns has what may be called a potential meaning acquired by its use during countless previous generations. As linguistic education develops in the child, and even in the adult, more and more of this total meaning of even common words may or may not be achieved. From this point of view, however, it is of course doubtful whether even most well educated adults ever come to define in a precise way many common and especially many abstract words. Almost all of us have special meanings of our own for such words as "freedom," "democracy," "responsibility," and "beauty," and when we hear them we sometimes think that the person who uses them means what we do. Unfortunately, this notion of communication is often something of an illusion.

We saw in the last lecture that anatomical study of the

preserved brain of an adult gorilla or a chimpanzee and of a man shows no sudden appearance of any new structure to account for the tremendous and unbridged gap between the adult intellectual powers of two of these three living anthropoids and the third. Somehow, sometime, as we have seen probably in the past few hundred thousand years, evolutionary processes have made man's brain only a little larger and more complex, but still just enough better than that of any other known living or fossil animal to make possible symbolic responses of the sort necessary in language and linguistically based thought processes. Man's linguistic processes are typically related in some respects to one side of the brain. The full extent of this functional dominance of one hemisphere over the other is not seen in animals below man. The brain structures, which make human concept formation and mathematical manipulation feasible, absolutely remove man forever from the level of all his infrahuman relatives. For, as Plato long ago pointed out, "the soul when thinking appears to me to be just talking–asking questions of herself and answering them, affirming and denying.... I say, then, that to form an opinion is to speak, and opinion is a word spoken, I mean, to one's self and in silence, not aloud or to another."

As thought, which includes this ability of the individual to talk silently to himself, develops, new and involved relationships are established between language processes and bodily activities and behavior. The child or even the adult individual sometimes talks subvocally to himself as he begins to learn a new motor skill such as driving a different automobile from the one to which he is accustomed. Involuntary responses of the body can be brought under subvocal verbal control. Many people can say to themselves, that is, think, "Squeeze that lemon for more juice," and their own mouths will water. Thought in such cases may not be merely subvocal speech but may also involve visual and even taste and smell imagery. Experiments in psychological laboratories have shown that by conditioned reflex techniques an individual can become able to say to himself "contract" or "dilate" and thus change the size of the pupils of his own eyes. If time allowed, it could be shown how these phenomena are related to certain aspects of what is now called psychosomatic medicine. Language in its relation to bodily states is therapeutically important in suggestion, in hypnosis, in psychoanalysis, and in some types of religious healing. Yoga, an Indian system of philosophy and way of life which is said to involve "the diversion of the senses from the external world and concentration on thought within," almost certainly employs the use of subvocal speech and of revived former sense impressions or images in relation to the neural control of breathing, heartbeat, and other organic processes. Here, indeed, in Plato's sense, one can learn to speak to one's self and learn to obey in strange ways. There can be little doubt that the brain activity related to subvocal speech and to imagery is at the base of many of the animistic theories mentioned at the start of this lecture.

Psychologists during recent years have been concerned in establishing a quantitative measurement of the continued growth of the capacity of the individual in childhood to make more and more effective external as well as internal responses on the basis of growing powers of language and the use of concepts and symbols. The Swiss psychologist Piaget has studied the gradual unfolding of the thought processes of young human beings as seen in their use of language. He has considered in detail the logic of childhood and the egocentric nature of much early human thought about causation, the nature of physical things, and other living organisms. In childhood subvocal speech and especially vivid imagery are not infrequently related, as in the creation of the imaginary companions that many lonely children think they know and with whom they play.

One general upshot of these and related studies seems to be a confirmation of the observation that there is a continuous development in the rate of growth in the fundamental capacity to use symbols, objective logic, and abstractions at least up to the period of adolescence. In many individuals during adolescence there is a change in the character of imagery and a flattening off of the rate of growth in other basic mental abilities. This does not, of course, mean that such young adults cease to have the capacity to learn new and complex ideas, abstract terms, or habits of response, but merely that after this period such individuals do not typically come to have any better or, indeed, quite the same physiological means of learning new responses or ideas than they had, for example, one year previously.

During the whole period of postnatal growth, emotional development and emotional learning go on together. At appropriate periods each individual learns to love himself, his parents and other people. As these stages pass the Freudian psychoanalysts have shown that all individuals generally develop complex nonconscious attachments of various sorts and strengths. These attachments, especially when they do not follow a normal pattern for a given society, may be the basis of mental illness even in adult life. These complex psychoanalytic theories are still being evaluated, but enough has been demonstrated to show that they are correct in holding that, in the evolution of the adult human mind, socially determined motives, some of which are not easily known even to the individual himself either in spoken or silent speech, play a large part. The relationship of these motives especially in regard to inner speech is basic in such great human powers as free choice of alternative courses of action and the courage that allows men and women to withstand pain and sometimes even to face death for subvocally held ideals.

As we have noted, one must not consider all thought, normal or abnormal, as being made up of language. Different individuals have different furniture, as it were, in their conscious processes. These show themselves in the constructive thought of reasoning and problem solving and in the self-centered or autistic thought of day and night dreams. Such processes often take on strange forms in mental illness. A stanza from an English poem of about 1615 dealing with Tom o'Bedlam illustrates the dynamics of a disturbed dream world:

> "With an host of furious fancies
> Whereof I am commander
> With a burning spear, and a horse of air,
> To the wilderness I wander.
> By a knight of ghosts and shadows
> I summoned am to tourney
> Ten leagues beyond the wide world's end.
> Methinks it is no journey."

In late maturity or old age a measurable decline or change in some but not necessarily all these basic mental capacities often occurs. In the growth and decline of mental powers one sees changes not only in the calculator-like aspects of mental ability, where they can be most easily demonstrated, but also in the long-term characteristics of personality such as in the basic urges related to reproduction and those called by the old term conscience or its new name, superego. All the processes, indeed, that give direction, style, and individuality to each unique total life and personality are modified with the years. Many of these changes seem to be related to alterations in the ductless glands of the body and in the circulatory system, but some are learned reactions and have a much more subtle emotional and intellectual base.

Some of the elements of mental life that are concerned in such processes as mechanical invention, artistic creation, physical courage, moral stamina, and spiritual understanding grow and decline in their own way during what has well been called the trajectory of life. It may be observed that experts in all intellectual fields, statistically speaking, do not do their best work at the same age. H. C. Lehman has recently demonstrated, in detailed studies of productive periods of mental life, that great mathematicians and physicists often make their most notable contributions early in adult life. Great historians and philosophers may flower intellectually even in old age. These observations seem to suggest something about the different mental processes required in these diverse fields. It may also indicate that social experience as contrasted with inborn physiological make-up may play different and subtle roles in producing the mental processes needed in different types of intellectual accomplishment.

I hope nothing I have said in this lecture implies that I believe that the full reaches of the adult human mind and spirit are in any way to be found in the early wriggles or reflex twitches of the fetus or the first pre-linguistic babblings of the infant; but, as I have tried to indicate, these early response, nevertheless, are not without deep significance. They may be even greater in importance than we now realize. Poets sometimes see where science has not yet penetrated. Coleridge years ago said, "Yes,—the history of a man for the nine months preceding his birth, would, probably, be far more interesting, and contain events of greater moment, than all the threescore and ten years that follow it."

Thus in individual development the mind of man emerges gradually as successive levels of maturation pass. Nerve cells become fully functional as they gain their insulating sheaths or, as it is called, become myelinated. Other subtle growth changes take place in the developing brain. Thus each person's hereditary character emerges as the inborn brain and body interact with the special environmental forces that the individual meets both before and after birth. As a result of the interplay of environmental stimuli on inborn and maturing structures, the physical basis of the mental processes of each individual develops.

The mental processes of the individual are for this reason never just the result of what germ plasm made them, nor are they ever a mere product of external physical and social forces. In some respects every mind is at each stage in its growth or decline a truly new em-

[73]

ergent "whole" or totality constructed by an almost in-
finitely complex interweaving of hereditary and environmental factors.

So far we have considered the emergence of mind as
if all minds were alike. Consideration of the growth of
any specific modern mind, however, would be incom-
plete without some reference to the fact that the mental
sphere is no contradiction to the law that diversity is
the most uniform thing in nature. Psychologists have
long and most properly been interested in why human
mental processes differ as they do from individual to
individual. Such knowledge is important when applied
to schools and to every other situation in which people
should be differentiated in terms of aptitudes and abilities. This knowledge of mental differences is also essential in any general description of any given mind in
health or disease. Only when one understands the limits
of mental capacity in large groups of people can the
average of these capacities be fully understood and the
individual compared with what is statistically typical
for a group. Individual human mental differences have
been studied, for example, in relation to averages for
both sexes, for those of the same remote ancestry or
near ancestry, as well as for age and many special environments.

The measurement of human mental differences in
connection with these factors is recognized as an important part of pure as well as applied psychology. So-

called tests of intelligence, to take but one example, have long been used in an attempt to differentiate between individuals and also to relate these discovered differences to group differences. These studies show, for example, that intelligence tests do not give any clear evidence that either adult men or women are superior in the possession of those qualities which are measured by such tests. Most studies also indicate that the school marks of boys and girls, when all subjects are averaged and selective factors guarded against, are about equal. In specific school subjects, girls on the average seem to excel boys in language studies, spelling, and color naming. Boys, on the other hand, seem to excel in physics, chemistry, and tests intended to measure intellectual ingenuity. No one knows for sure whether these differences are learned or socially determined or whether they have a true biological base. It is true also that in studies of unusually gifted children more boys than girls have been found in the groups that have been assembled by tests. The ratio is about one hundred and twenty boys to one hundred girls. Why this is, however, no one can yet say with assurance. It must be admitted also that it seems true that in general there are more men than women in institutions for the care of the mentally deficient.

In our society women, as compared with men, tend to be more interested in persons than in things. Studies show that women on the average are more religious, more sympathetic, and, according to certain observations, more patient than men. There is some suggestion that men appreciate humor more generally than do women; but there are many exceptions to these general trends. Why are there even these apparent average differences? No one yet knows. Probably these differences are both culturally and biologically caused. Certainly, references to group averages are important enough to be considered by one who would understand any specific adult mind.

Almost everything that has been learned about the difficulty of studying mental characteristics of individuals as related to the simple fact that the person in question is a man or woman can be said about the attempt to refer to individuals any measured average of characteristics of remote ancestral groups of the sort commonly described as the races of mankind.

The influence of family or of immediate ancestry is also important but difficult to measure in the determination of individual mental characteristics. If one undertakes a study of men in a socially stable community, members of some families will often be seen to demonstrate through a series of generations the possession of special personality characteristics. In the United States Senate at the present time are a number of men who come from families that have been prominent in public service in the country since the early 1600's. In recent years it has been fashionable to try to explain all such familial differences as caused by advantageous environmental factors; but now the power of heredity is again being recognized as important in such studies. In considering inheritance, physical and mental, one must always remember that the bodies and minds of infants come not from their own parents' bodies and minds but from ancestral paternal and maternal germ cells just, in fact, as did their own parents'. To put this in another way, parents, like children, are a product of paternal and maternal germ cell strains. That some such strains have special biological characteristics that are basic at least to certain mental superiorities or limitations now seems quite certain.

The study of identical twins has long interested psychologists in this connection. Especially if twins are reared apart, the scientist may gain considerable insight into the relative importance of heredity and environment in the determination of physical and mental characteristics by measuring these individuals as they grow up. In general, the make-up of identical twins, even when reared apart, indicates that in intelligence and other measurable mental characteristics these individuals are somewhat more similar than are ordinary brothers or sisters. It is also true that, on the average, foster children are less like their parents in measured mental characteristics than are such parents' own children. Here again in psychology we are face to face with a problem to which many nonprofessional individuals give categorical answers but to which the scientist must still raise a danger flag and say, "The evidence is not yet all in."

In a democracy the idea that certain family strains are likely to produce individuals of higher intelligence and of greater mental stamina and energy than do other family strains is not always emphasized. However, provided a society is sufficiently fluid to give every proper opportunity to able individuals when they do arise from unexpected sources, it may be that the recognition of genetic excellence will sometime be considered as not unimportant in maintaining a good and free society. Our western economy is becoming so complex and so based on intricate thought and advanced science that all its people must depend on the limited number of minds in each generation that can use the symbols of mathematics or of language effectively for the maintenance of their health, their standard of living and, in time of war, their survival.

I have already emphasized the fact that maturity, independent of all other factors, plays an important role in the mental reactions that ought to be expected at particular stages of life. In the Bible, in Shakespeare's famous seven ages, and in much general literature we find a correct recognition of the fact that infancy, youth, middle age, and old age all have their special mental characteristics, some of which are assets and some liabilities. Here again, however, it is surprisingly difficult to demonstrate by measurement that a given individual follows the course that can be shown for the group as a whole. Some very old men retain a youthfulness of mental outlook and, for example, show an ability to memorize that is superior to that possessed by some other individuals many years younger. Here, as in all considerations of group differences, we must remember how dangerous it is to argue from the generality of old men to particular old individuals, but this must not keep us from considering the general or average characteristics of each age group. The psychologically doubtful modern pressure to establish fixed retirement at sixty or sixty-five years of age without regard to human individual differences attests how hard it is to deal with individuals and not with groups.

The influence of environmental forces in producing the unique pattern of each mental life is, of course, of fundamental importance in understanding the making of any individual modern mind. No matter what inborn aptitudes a person may have, his mental capacities will not ordinarily show themselves unless, as a child, he or she grew up in an environment that allowed these capacities to develop. Thus, anyone who wishes to demonstrate that in the adult human mind there are no characteristics that are wholly the result of inheritance can always make his point; but it is also increasingly clear that it can be shown that inheritance limits and in subtle ways directs each individual's mental life as it matures.

[79]

The speed of reaction time, the nature of immediate memory, and mental characteristics commonly called by such names as attention, persistence, and ability in problem solving and in the use of abstract concepts may well have a genetic base. It is impossible today, in view of existing scientific evidence, to assert that the measured differences between individuals in these and hundreds of other characteristics are alone the results of individual experience or of personal education. Modern statistical study of test results by the technique known as factor analysis has isolated certain so-called primary mental factors. A study of these factors, which include such processes as verbal comprehension, perceptual speed, and immediate memory, shows that these factors do not all mature at the same time or at the same rate. Most of these factors have reached the adult state by the age of nineteen.

In everyday life we do not often analyze the mental lives of total individuals. We do not think of component patterns of superiorities and inferiorities in sub-processes. Rather, we assess the minds, as we say, of whole individuals in relation to the general way in which they act in industrial and social life. A handsome, agreeable, but intellectually slightly dull man may succeed in many walks of life to almost exactly the same degree as a physically unattractive, bright, and irascible man. Society may pay both such individuals the same yearly salary. Who will say which has the better mind or who can be sure that education made the basic difference between the two personalities? The mechanisms of electric and of gas refrigerators are very different, but the consumer judges them not by their hidden functions but by what they do. This is often also true of the practical man's judgment of the minds of his associates.

It seems to me, therefore, that during the last generation social scientists, educators, and even psychologists have tended to overemphasize the influence of certain qualities as contrasted with others in their assessment of adult minds and the environmental factors that undoubtedly color them all. Recent studies of extremes in mental ability make many individuals sure that heredity as well as environment must be considered if we are to understand at all adequately the making of any real individual modern mind. Essentially all the data with which I am now acquainted seem to demonstrate that the basic causal factors in severe mental disease are physiological. Such factors may well be related to the largely inborn constitution of the individual rather than to the specific stresses or strains or emotional difficulties encountered by the individual during his growth and education. Studies bearing on this question have been made of the number of individuals affected by various serious types of mental illness during periods of general political and economic stress such as prolonged wars, disasters, and revolutions. Every such study that I know about has demonstrated that the number of individuals affected by serious mental disease in relation to the total population remains relatively constant in spite of the stresses of violent environmental disturbances. These facts have a general implication. They suggest that fundamental traits in normal as well as in abnormal human mental life such as a placid or uneven temperament, energy, persistence, problem solving ability, and immediate memory may owe much of their measured characteristics to processes which would not be as they are except for the individual's chromosomes.

Therefore, it seems that individual modern minds may differ from each other partly because of sex, remote ancestry, near ancestry, age, and environment. This consideration leads to the conclusion that the educator and the social worker must not expect the wrong things from schools or from new social or economic reforms.

Every individual human being has certain combinations of characteristics because of the unique inherited and environmental factors which have made him or her what he or she is. The never-ending charm of biography and autobiography as well as of fiction is largely dependent on the infinite variety of relationships between motives, experiences, and constant and so-called chance factors in the environment that build each mind and thus form a basis for the human interplay between such minds. Shakespeare, Thackeray, Trollope, and many other writers who have the skill to show what are called the "secrets of the human heart" are in one sense great psychologists. These creative artists sometimes see individual mental lives and the complexly interweaving factors that make them in a subtle and delicate way that cannot be expected of psychologists or psychoanalysts who must concern themselves with the general principles which are illustrated in individual lives. It is for this reason that the modern novelist who reads a little of the works of Freud and then tries to construct a character based on psychoanalysis is apt to create not a person but a wax figure moved by strange springs and motors. In this lecture, therefore, an effort is made to show some of the factors that make all normal adult civilized human minds.

Modern experimental psychology, nevertheless, has derived from the study of prenatal life and human infancy and from the investigation of infrahuman mammals a knowledge of the way in which each mind grows in the race and in the individual. Comparative psychology has demonstrated that many animals below man learn and profit by instruction and by individual experience. In man alone, however, because of his high ability in the use of abstract ideas, symbols, and writing, each generation in some respects, but not in all, may stand on the shoulders of all preceding generations.

An example may make this point more clear. The make-up of any modern mind and, indeed, the probable nature of the human mind in the future may be made more vivid if we compare mental life in superior and

well-educated civilized modern western men and women with the minds of similar individuals in the high
period of Athens. There seem to be at least three great
differences between the superior minds that have done
so much for mankind in these two periods. First, the
modern mind has available for its use a great body of
tested and organized knowledge that was unknown in
classic times. In a very real sense this knowledge con-
structs or is basic to each mind. Second, modern man
has the advantage of many inventions of physical appa-
ratus such as the electron microscope, to take but one
example, to assist his senses and thus his perceptual
powers. Third, the modern mind has available new intellectual processes suchas present-day mathematics to
help make thinking quick, correct, and constructive.
The art forms that have developed in recent centuries
allow a broader expression of genius than was true before their invention. One has only to compare the modern symphony with the music of antiquity to see what
this progress has meant.

As a result of these developments, modern minds
that may be inferior in intrinsic capacities, when compared with the minds of such men as Plato and Aristotle,
are, nevertheless, more powerful in many respects than
were the minds of these superlatively great men. For
example, what Plato and Aristotle said about astronomy
or physiology today is interesting only because it is
quaint. But what these philosophers have to say about

man's social living, politics, and a wide range of human values still in part seems to have been written today and to be full of profound current wisdom.

Why is this? In my opinion this distinction does not merely mean, as has so often been said, that the social sciences are backward—the retarded children as it were of the intellectual world—but rather that there is a deeper reason for this difference which may be related to the make-up of the human mind itself. In these lectures an effort has been made to show that some aspects and especially some of the limitations of man's mind are old and probably unchanged, at least in all the generations known during historic time. Other aspects of mind are ever new, as at that great dawn or cosmic emergence when true language was developed or at a much later time, to take but one of many possible examples, when in mathematics the calculus was invented.

Is it not possible that the hectic and often iconoclastic enlightenment of the eighteenth century and the destructive intellectual forces set on fire by the French Revolution tried too rapidly to tear down the good as well as the bad in the old human customs, social traditions, and even benign superstitions which up to that time had slowly evolved through the ages? These ideological changes, when combined with the population shifts and the human rootlessness caused by the industrial revolution, may have been too rapid to allow the slow procedures of trial and error and social testing to work out new patterns of interpersonal relationships which could be truly satisfying to the conservative limitations of man's mental processes. It is not easy by any type of speculative theorizing to change quickly and also successfully the essential reinforcements of behavior that have made most old societies stable and successful.

Our age may thus well examine with care the ways in which basic human patterns of living and values have arisen, or have been discovered in the past. Is it not possible that as we make this study we will find in a new way how important are the insights and the patterning of life that come from participation in a mature and organized religion in helping individuals and groups of individuals to maintain the steady, tested, and, I am tempted to say, essentially unchanging values of human life? Is it not conceivable that this knowledge may indicate ways of achieving anew the integration of the old and the novel in mental and derivatively in social life? In this way peace may be brought to the modern mind that wordly theorizing alone with all its self-conscious rationalism has never given.

These last paragraphs I am sure have raised more questions than they have answered. But if they have hinted at problems about the emergence and the inner nature of the modern mind that are worthy of further study my present task will have at least been partly accomplished. We have seen that the modern study of

CONTENTS

Part I

TEACHING AND TEACHER

Chapter 1

REALISTIC UTOPIANISM

"The message of Jesus, as I understand it, is contained in the *Sermon on the Mount*. . . . It is that *Sermon* which has endeared Jesus to me," wrote Mahatma Gandhi.[1]

A good many Jews can repeat that statement just as sincerely as they can accept Gandhi's subsequent criticism: "The message, to my mind, has suffered distortion in the West. . . . Much of what passes as Christianity is a negation of the *Sermon on the Mount*."[2]

Karl Marx too asked the Christians of his day, "Does not your practical life continually give the lie to your theory?. . . Do you turn your right cheek to someone who slaps you on the left, or don't you rather file suit for assault and battery? But the gospel forbids it."[3]

In fact, the history of the impact of the Sermon on the Mount can largely be described in terms of an attempt to domesticate everything in it that is shocking, demanding, and uncompromising, and render it harmless. "Time and time again," writes Günther Bornkamm, "Christianity, especially with the assistance of its theology, has known so well and still knows how to intercept, so to speak, the thrust of Jesus' challenge, to divert it and to settle down peacefully in spite of it."[4]

Even in the contemporary peace debate, speakers and writers find the Sermon on the Mount an easy weapon with which to beat an opponent over the head, without taking the trouble to find out what is actually written there.

In fact even the experts have frequently come up with odd

conclusions. Martin Luther, for example, did not hesitate to say that the Sermon on the Mount does not belong in city hall, for "one cannot govern" with it. Former German Chancellor Helmut Schmidt, speaking at a Protestant *Kirchentag* in Hamburg, doubted that any "political guidelines" could be derived from the Sermon on the Mount. "No state can be ruled by the Sermon on the Mount," said Otto von Bismarck. What he meant was that not having a conscience, which Hitler called "a Jewish invention," made the pursuit of power politics much easier. Whether today we can still manage *without* the spirit of the Sermon on the Mount is doubtful; but to go *against* it would be to invite catastrophe.

Karl Barth, the Swiss theologian, even held that to construct a picture of the Christian life from the directives in the Sermon on the Mount has always proved impossible. "It would be sheer folly to interpret the imperatives of the Sermon on the Mount as if we should bestir ourselves to actualize these pictures."[5]

His compatriot Leonhard Ragaz thought otherwise; in 1945 he began his exegesis of the Sermon on the Mount with the words: "The Sermon on the Mount will emerge again. Ever stronger. Ever more vital."

Today this prophecy of the Swiss socialist is beginning to be fulfilled—and the eight chief misinterpretations of the sermon still accompany it.

EIGHT MISINTERPRETATIONS

The first might be called the perfectionist conception. It sees the Sermon on the Mount as a list of supercommandments announcing loudly and clearly: This is what you must do to be blessed; beatitude does not come any cheaper. Such a view reflects an exaggerated legalism, which Paul and Luther would reject as gross heresy. Worse, it is a textbook example of the infamous "works justification" theory, which holds that salvation can be earned by deeds, and tries to build its own ladder to heaven. The Sermon on the Mount is "Mosissimus Moses," to use Luther's phrase—that is, the epitome of inflexible legalism.

The second is the theory of unrealizability, based on the idea that all these demands are really superhuman, their sole purpose being to drum into human beings their own inadequacies. According to this interpretation, the Sermon on the Mount is inflicted on them to make them stumble. At that point, convinced of their need of redemption and deeply contrite, they will be prepared to hear God's word of merciful forgiveness.

In the words of Gerhard Kittel:

> The meaning of the Sermon on the Mount is: Demolish! It can only tear down. In the long run it has only one purpose: to expose and exhibit the great poverty in empiric human beings.[6]

To put it another way: "This is what you ought to do, you wretched weakling, but you can't succeed, as you well know. That is why you need God's gracious love for everything you undertake."

A third theory, invoking "interim ethics," can be described as last-minute panic. It sees the Sermon on the Mount as a summons to one final exertion before the imminent catastrophe of the Last Judgment. "Now pull yourself together one last time, you poor devil, before it's too late!" That is what is written between the lines, for even tomorrow the days of divine grace may come to an end. But the fact that Jesus erred in his intense expectation of the immediate passing of this world and the advent of the "reign of heaven" as a completely new beginning—as has since been conceded by many reputable theologians—threatens to rob this apocalyptical interpretation of relevance for today.

A fourth explanation compares the imperatives of the Sermon on the Mount with the sober realpolitik of the past four thousand years of world history and—with an audible sigh of relief—concludes that it rests on a moral reverie that can confidently be written off as utopian. Utopia is used here in the literal sense: as something without place, not of this world, homeless on our earth, and so of no consequence whatever for practical politics.

A fifth explanation asserts that the Sermon on the Mount holds only for the narrow circle of Jesus' disciples and calls only them to emulate him. A curtain of salvific distance descends between our contemporary world and the Galilee of that time, allowing a worldly-wise urbanity to remove the critical barb from the text and dismiss the demands of the sermon as naive figures of speech.

A sixth approach rests on the romantic radicalism that is determined to bypass the complexity of life with a few simple but splendid claims. The Sermon on the Mount is elevated to a timeless, universally valid manual of ethics for humanity, demanding everything but at bottom imposing nothing.

A seventh explanation sees here a pointer toward a correct attitude in the private sphere as an aid to a correct relationship with God. Looked at from this perspective, the Sermon on the Mount presents an especially fine superethic, an end in itself for self-centered perfection, society being merely a tool for individual redemption.

An eighth reading is offered by the historian, who, aware of the historical circumstances of a small, subjugated Jewish state squeezed to the very brink of extinction between Roman brutality and Zealot violence, soberly deduces from the Sermon on the Mount a positive, practical program. Here are the peace tactics, "wise as a serpent and gentle as a dove," of a worldly-wise strategist, Jesus, who repudiates both hopeless war against the Roman superpower and fainthearted desertion of the cause in favor of liberating his people from the Roman yoke through nonviolent resistance.

"Be brief in your prayers," we read just before the Our Father. One possible meaning: put off the litanies until peaceful times, for in time of need God also hears the quick but fervent cry.

If someone compels you to go a mile with him, then go two! The reference here is to the Roman compulsory labor policy, where only meekness can move the brutal tyrant to sufferance.

Absolutizing fraternal love, removing all causes of intra-Jewish contentiousness, humility before the persecutor, and inalienable solidarity—all these can also be interpreted as indispensable emergency measures needed to steel the national spirit of resistance against long, bloody oppression.

All these explanations seem defective or false to me because they neglect the two principal characteristics of Jesus' preaching, which run like a double thread through his entire teaching: first, taking God with the utmost seriousness, which inspired in him a healthy discontent with any halfway measures or compromises, and, secondly, the realism of one who, knowing human nature profoundly, did indeed pursue a radical theo-politics, but by means of pragmatic, doable methods, which never make excessive demands on persons of good will who collaborate with God.

Hence, Jesus goes all the way and climbs aloft to a solitary peak, which seems absolutely unattainable. This we may concede, yet to aspire to the unattainable is perhaps what is most human in our species. It is certainly the quintessence of Judaism. For this small nation of incorrigible optimists, of which the preacher on the mount was a member, has time and again let itself be carried away out of the painful experience of the eternal chasm between ideal and reality into spiritual adventures that have settled many a utopia on earth.

After all, is not the entire progress of humanity but one long series of realized utopias? Certainly there has been no lack of disappointments and failures. But despite all frustration, vigorous hope remains the most Jewish of all emotions—the irrepressible urge to make yesterday's dream tomorrow's reality.

To Jews a pseudo-realism that accepts the status quo as final and unchangeable seems false. Genuine realism, in contrast, is the restlessness of those thirsting for salvation, the impatience roaring and blowing through the Sermon on the Mount; it is the sister of the "Jewish haste" that steadfastly refuses to call today good or to sanctify any status quo. Passionately aware of the defectiveness of all human works, the summons goes forth here to improve this world, to discipline oneself, and to gain the promised future that is and remains the goal of the entire Bible.

JESUS THE JEW

For me Jesus is less the founder of Christianity than the instigator of a Christian way of life that has its great manifesto in the Sermon on the Mount: a Christian way of life that at bottom amounts to a Jewish way of life and, like it, unfortunately, finds far too few imitators in either community of faith.

A man comes forth in Israel to make today's prophetic vision tomorrow's agenda; one for whom the teachings of Mount Sinai do not suffice because he wishes to penetrate beyond to the original divine intent; one who, despite war and tyranny, dares to pursue the biblical love of neighbor to its ultimate consequence in order to brand all our souls with an ideal of human possibility that no longer allows us to be content with the threadbare, run-of-the-mill persons we are but need not be.

It is an attainable ideal, a realistic utopia, one that need not remain on paper if believing Jews summon up the courage to transcend themselves, to reach beyond themselves, to become greater and more human in the tireless imitation of God that Judaism counts the most sacred of all commandments. In all this messianic urgency toward the humanization God wills for all the children of Adam and toward the humanization of this earth, in the deathless power of hope that finds in reliance on "the above" the courage to go "forward," Jesus of Nazareth was "the central Jew," as Martin Buber called him, the one who spurs us all to emulation.

"Whoever meets Jesus Christ meets Judaism." Pope John Paul II, during his visit to Mainz, adopted as his own this opening sentence of the declaration of the Catholic bishops of West Germany (April 28, 1980), "On the Relationship of the Church to Judaism."

What particularly stands out here is that Jesus' belonging to the people of Israel is not simply a matter of genetics but is revealed especially in his spiritual world and his moral teachings.

The unavoidable consequence of these facts is that everything Jesus said and accomplished, did and did not do, on earth discloses its full meaning only when seen against his profound Jewishness.

Another insight, one derived from Martin Luther, fits here. In his *Table Talk* we read:

> The Hebrew language is the very best and the richest in words, and pure; it does not go begging, has its own coloring, defies replication. . . . If I were younger, I would learn this language, because without it Scripture can never be understood correctly. The New Testament, although written in Greek, is full of Hebraisms and Hebrew expressions. So it is rightly said: The Hebrews drink from the fount and the Greeks from the brooklets that flow from the fount; but the Latins drink from the puddles.[7]

Jesus' Jewishness and the fundamentally Hebraic quality of his glad tidings should be a twofold guide in getting behind the translation-Greek of the evangelist and as close as possible to the original meaning of the masterpiece of Jesus' ethical teachings.

THE TEACHING OF THE PREACHER ON THE MOUNT

Here, an unavoidable digression. In the Sermon on the Mount are we dealing with Jesus' own words, or is the text partly, or even mostly, a literary creation of the evangelist?

To what extent can we find the stuff of Jesus' teaching in these three chapters in Matthew (5:1–7:29)? Can we distinguish what came from the mouth of the Nazarene and what from the pen of Matthew? Or has the primitive community of faith developed the ideas of its Master further and extrapolated from them? Has Matthew drawn on the sermon on the plain in Luke's Gospel—or is it the other way around?

Has the evangelist created his text from a preexistent collection of the sayings, *logia*, of Jesus, or attempted to reconcile contradictory traditions, or even given his own imagination free rein? And, not least, in the process of translation into Greek, what was altered, what was misunderstood, what was added and omitted?

Question upon question—to all of which New Testament scholarship can give only approximate and partial answers. Helpful in this endeavor to reach back to the *ipsissima vox* are such characteristics of Jesus' speaking style as his hyperbole, paradox, the pulse of his lifelike expressions, his attention to compelling imagery, but above all the passages that, when translated back into Galilean Aramaic (or the Hebrew of the first century), yield memorable wordplays or rhythmically constructed verses easy to commit to memory.

In the end we shall never know how immediately and directly Jesus speaks to us here. Only one thing is certain: the uniform structure of this discourse, the power of faith that it radiates, and the world-affirming spirit that blows into our face here—all these strengthen the impression that this is the original creation of one of the great luminaries of human history. Despite any secondary redaction, and even after two millennia, it has suffered little or no loss of its perennial dynamism.

"What is good in the New Testament is not new, and what is new is not good," was the judgment of Jewish circles dealing with the Gospels on a scholarly basis for the first time around the turn of this century. Julius Wellhausen, the famous biblical scholar, went even further: "Everything in the Sermon on the Mount can be found in the Talmud—yes, and how much more besides!" The outstanding corroboration of this opinion is furnished by Paul Billerbeck who, in his monumental five-volume *Kommentar zum Neuen Testament aus Talmud und Midrasch*, compiled no fewer than 309 pages of rabbinic parallels and analogues to the three chapters of the Sermon on the Mount. But we certainly do not need Billerbeck's admirable compilation to test out the possibility that a Jewish Sermon on the Mount, which would strike the reader as a paraphrase of Matthew 5–7, can be put together without using a single word from Jesus.

And yet, such a paraphrase is possible only because we do possess Jesus' Sermon on the Mount. For the fact that the plaster, the cement, and all the building stones come from Jewish quarries in no way diminishes the greatness of the architect who has used these raw materials to design and erect his own moral code.

After all, Beethoven did not invent a single new note to compose the Ninth Symphony, his immortal masterpiece.

Chapter 2

PREAMBLE
(Matt. 5:1-2, 17-20)

Now to the principal statements of the text, as read by Jewish eyes through Hebrew lenses!

THE MOUNT

When he saw the multitude, he climbed up on the mount, and when he had sat down, his disciples approached him. And he opened his mouth and taught them, saying . . . [Matt. 5:1-2].

The clumsiness of the Greek, intent on imitating the Hebrew word order and sentence structure, attests that already in the introduction we are standing on Semitic literary soil. This enables us to deduce from these two framework sentences the outline of a theological program.

In the Hebrew Bible we hear of a whole series of mountains—Zion in Jerusalem, Hermon in the north, Tabor, Carmel, and Gilboa. But when a Jew hears of *the* mountain, with no further qualifications, then there is not doubt that it is the Mount Sinai of the law being alluded to.

It is not by chance that Jesus is compared to Moses eighteen times in the Gospels, beginning with the garlands of legends woven around the birth of each of them, the death of the innocents in Bethlehem reminiscent of the killing of all the Hebrew boys by the pharaoh, through the flight into Egypt, the exodus from the land

11

of the Nile, the forty days (years) of temptation in the wilderness, even to the mountain of the Transfiguration where Moses appeared to Jesus. Everywhere these parallels from salvation history resonate.

Both men climb up *the* mount to let the God-given teaching resound from the heights. Because Jesus leaves the multitude behind him, just like Moses who was commanded "not to allow the people to go up with him" (Exod. 24:2), the question of who is being addressed by the Sermon arises. The text answers: his disciples, who, "approached" him—a verb that Matthew uses not infrequently to emphasize their closeness to Jesus.

The "multitude" serves only as a living background—at the beginning of the Sermon on the Mount as mute extras in a play (Matt. 5:1), and at the end as amazed and "astonished" listeners (Matt. 7:28). They are thus symbolic, like those at the foot of Sinai, representatives of Israel at least in an allusive way.

Finally, for a small selective audience it is significant that Jesus sat down before he "opened his mouth," as it says here in good Hebrew (cf. Ps. 81:11).

INSTRUCTION

In the case of a rabbi—and the evangelists give Jesus that title no fewer than fourteen times—the sitting posture points unequivocally to an instruction, which, according to the rules of the great Torah schools, always takes place seated. So, for example, the scribes and the Pharisees "sit on the seat of Moses" (Matt. 23:2) and Jesus himself "sat and taught daily in the temple" (Matt. 26:55). We still use the expression "chair" in reference to a university professorship.

Parables or Bible-reading, on the other hand, are delivered standing: "and he stood up to read" (Luke 4:16). Important too is the distinction that teaching in rabbinical practice always is given only to a small circle of initiated disciples, whereas the great addresses are directed to "the many," as it is often put, and usually in the form of parables, understandable even to shepherds and tillers of the soil.

So we have to do here with an instruction rather than a sermon, as we also hear in the concluding passage: "The multitudes were astonished at his *teaching,* for he *taught* them as one who had authority" (Matt. 7:28f.).

The multitude may indeed have listened in the background, but the immediate target audience of the entire talk was the circle of twelve, who were then to knead the dough intended for the people. This gives us an important indication of Jesus' pedagogy and of the manner in which he planned to carry through his repentance movement—a repentance movement aimed at hastening the coming of the reign of heaven.

Those who would reproach Jesus with "Jewish particularism" are answered by Rabbi Leo Baeck:

> It bears witness to the power of the words of Jesus rather than indicating any narrowness of outlook, that he limited his message to Israel. But is is fortunate that his exhortation is neither in the Old Testament nor in the Talmud, for it would have found small grace in the eyes of those austere Protestants who would have dubbed it as yet another manifestation of the narrow-minded national religion of the Jews. . . . The prophets speak of the world and its salvation, but they speak to Israel.[8]

In the end it appears that in the Instruction on the Mount Jesus had in mind a public of three concentric circles: he first enjoins the ethos of God's dominion on his community of disciples, "the little flock" (Luke 12:32), which is open to all Israel, which he is then resolved to gather together without exception, along with all his "lost sheep," to make it finally "a light unto the nations so that you may be my salvation to the ends of the earth" (Isa. 49:6).

A NEW TEACHING?

The question that *must* obtrude on every Jewish reader, for whom Matthew—or his predecessor—originally wrote this Gospel, is whether a new teaching is being proclaimed here in opposition to, or even in place of, the Torah of Sinai. In order to nip this suspicion in the bud, Jesus begins with a vigorous emphasis on the eternal validity of all the commandments of Sinai.

But Jesus is in no way satisfied with a mere declaration of

principle; instead he not only calls attention to his fidelity to the Torah with a triple formulation, but also seeks to disarm any reproaches whatsoever that his daring biblical exegesis is an attempt to annul the original meaning of scripture:

Do not think I have come to destroy the law or the prophets. I have not come to destroy but to fulfill. For I say to you truly: until heaven and earth pass away, not one dot or one stroke will disappear from the law until everything is accomplished. Whoever breaks one of the least commandments and teaches others to do likewise will be called the least in the realm of heaven; but whoever keeps and teaches them will be called great in the realm of heaven [Matt. 5:17–19].

In all rabbinic literature I know of no more unequivocal, fiery acknowledgment of Israel's holy scripture than this opening to the Instruction on the Mount.

Jesus is here more radical even than Rabbi Hiyya bar Abba and Rabbi Johanan, both of whom were prepared to renounce a letter—that is, a written character—of the Torah if doing so would publicly sanctify the name of God (see Yeb 79a).

Here it also becomes clear that Matthew saw his Master not as a new lawgiver but as the legitimate interpreter of God's will as contained in the Torah. Jesus is no anti-Moses to Matthew, but rather one who carries on from Moses who had begun to expound the teaching of Sinai in his own time: "Moses began to expound this Torah" (Deut. 1:5). The "people of the book," who celebrated even their greatest kings as interpreters of scripture, would necessarily also expect their Messiah to be a teacher of Torah. In fact, this expectation went so far that in Jesus' lifetime one spoke of a "Torah of the Messiah"—not a new Torah, but a new explanation of the eternal instruction of Sinai, which would reveal all the riches of that spiritual treasury, disclose its fundamental intention, and solve all the puzzles hidden in it.

Jesus neither destroyed nor misappropriated this Torah. On the contrary, he confirmed and affirmed it. Although he urged its highest fulfillment through the development of its original ethics, he, like many other rabbis, suggested his own exegesis—the radical demand of love, the center of Jesus' ethic.

The word "radical" comes from *radix*—source, stem, or root; Jesus wishes to penetrate to the roots of the Torah. They are for him the key to God's dominion. And not only for him.

Rabbi Simlai said: "Do you wish to know that all God's ways are love? In the beginning of the Torah he adorned a bride (Gen. 2:22), at its end he buried a dead man (Deut. 34:6), and in the middle he visited a sick man (Gen. 18:1)" (Tanhuma Wayera I). Rabbi Akiba said: "Love your neighbor as yourself! (Lev. 19:18). That is the great principal rule of the Torah!" (Sifre Lev. 19:18).

Rabbi Jesus merged the two—love of God and love of neighbor—into one great double commandment (Mark 12:28-34) in which he saw the fullness of God's will animating the entire Torah.

Martin Luther acknowledged this fact: "The law is of itself so rich and perfect that one must do nothing to it. . . . Thus no one, even Christ himself, can improve the law."[9] "Christ did not abolish the law, but rather he interpreted it."[10]

Calvin too indicated his aversion to understanding Jesus as a revealer of a new law; he was "no second Moses" and his work was "in no way an improved lawgiving."[11]

For Nicholas of Lyra, keeping the Ten Commandments suffices for attainment of salvation, for Jesus "brought no new moral law but rather gave the decalogue its original meaning."[12]

The Instruction on the Mount is thus nothing but the Torah exegesis of Jesus of Nazareth proceeding from this twofold love and aiming to make it concrete so that God's reign on earth may break through. To clarify this insight, three translation errors must be corrected.

TORAH

First of all, Jesus did not say "law" but "Torah," which means "directive" or "teaching." The word has more a sense of promise, fulfillment, salvation history, and ethos about it than of actual law and rule, which supposedly leads to "arid legalism" or "sterile formalism," as many Christian biblical commentaries assert even today.

This Bible of Jesus and earliest Christianity is primarily and principally *evangelium* in the Christian sense of the word—the

good news of God's love and of the God-given freedom of a Jew.
Any freedom, however, that does not willingly take upon itself "the
yoke of the realm of heaven," as the rabbis call their godly instruction, leads inevitably to anarchy and self-enslavement to all the
carnality and brutishness that is still simmering and raging in
human hearts.

What this Torah means to Jews—and Jesus' Jewishness is also
essential to christology—can be read from the daily liturgy of the
synagogue, where Jesus preached. One of its central blessings
celebrates the giving of the Torah, which led to Israel's becoming a
people. But this blessing is not called "revelation" or "instruction"
or even "law," but *ahaba*—"love." For it is the fullness of heavenly
love, which expressed itself in the gracious gift of Torah, for which
Jews give thanks daily:

> Thou hast loved the house of Israel with everlasting love;
> thou hast taught us Torah and precepts, laws and judgments.
> Therefore, Lord our God, when we lie down and when we
> rise up we will speak of thy laws, and rejoice in the words of
> thy Torah and in thy precepts for evermore. Indeed, they are
> our life and the length of our days. . . . Mayest thou never
> take away thy love from us.

In other words, without the liberating good news of the exodus
there would be no Sinai of the divine commandments. But without
Sinai and its decalogue there would be no active, lived faith. For
just as the Jew cannot imagine this world without God, nor imagine
Israel without the wide world it is appointed to serve, so too love
and commandment are not a contradiction but a harmony, for the
Torah was given out of love and out of love it is observed. "Its ways
are the ways of grace," the liturgy says of Torah, "and all its paths
lead to peace." Three millennia of strong Jewish faith and a positive
attitude toward the world have ratified this statement.

And yet in all religions bound to inspired scriptures there have
been and still are the ultrapious and the fundamentalists, those
who, like Famulus Wagner, do not strive for the spirit but instead
prefer "what is written in black and white," which they can "buy
with confidence."

How does a "book religion" guard itself against the danger of theological arteriosclerosis? The rabbinic answer stands on three legs. First, Deuteronomy avers seven times "By these command-ments you should *live*"; the verb at the end of this sentence is seen by the Talmudic fathers as a call for continual reinterpretation of scripture in order to promote and enhance human life, which is its central concern.

Secondly, the peerless sanctity of human life enters in—a princi-ple that can be viewed as the guiding star of all Hebrew legislation. To save one's own or another's life, or to preserve it from presumed grave danger, any commandment—except three—not only can but even should be broken, in that particular instance. In the word of the Talmud, "If anyone preserves a single life, it is credited to him as if he had saved the whole world."

The third safety valve against legalistic paralysis is the presuppo-sition that seventy exegetical possibilities are inherent in every biblical text—seventy interpretations after the symbolic number of that worldwide oikoumene of peoples listed in Genesis 10, all standing alongside one another as equals, like the nations of this earth. For there is, after all, no Jewish pope in a position to elevate one particular interpretation to orthodoxy or dogma, and de-nounce the remaining sixty-nine.

"All seventy stand valid before God," runs an adage that was old when Jesus came into the world. This hermeneutic diversity is reinforced by the nature of Hebrew, which is written without vowels in a kind of consonant-shorthand. It frequently permits one and the same word to be read and to be understood in two or three different ways without altering even a single dot or stroke of the Torah, as Rabbi Jesus correctly forbade (Matt. 5:18).

It is this God-given freedom of exegesis that has permitted rabbis of every generation to reinterpret the biblical text when necessary to preserve fidelity to the biblical spirit. One example, representa-tive of many, may clarify this practice.

According to the biblical commandment (Deut. 15:1-6), at the end of every seventh year all outstanding debts should be waived. This statute was intended for the benefit of the poor, widows, orphans, and strangers in a predominantly agrarian society. But in the course of its development toward urban early capitalism, it happened that toward the end of the seven-year limit it was next to impossible for the poor to get a loan.

When the sage Hillel, whom some scholars number among the teachers of the young Jesus, came to realize that what had originally worked in favor of social welfare now led to completely opposite results, he found a solution that had five effects: (1) it protected the creditors from exploitation by debtors; (2) it guarded against violation of the commandment (Deut. 15:9); (3) it facilitated borrowing by the poor before and during the year of the rescript of debts; (4) it did contradict the strict meaning of the biblical law, but, not least (5), it adapted the basic social intention of scripture to new social circumstances.

Jesus' Instruction on the Mount is at home in this climate of flexible fidelity to Torah, which, while trying to do justice to the deep meaning of scripture, shuns any constricting adherence to the letter.

"FULFILLMENT"

A second error in translation concerns the verb "fulfill," which, when used in connection with the Torah, is alien to the Semitic spirit of the language. Although the verb "dissolve," in the sense of "abolish" or "repeal," is familiar in Jewish linguistic usage, for Jews it is the words (1) "keep" (Matt. 19:17), (2) "do" (Rom. 2:12), or (3) "establish" in the same sense of (4) "make effective" (Rom. 3:31) that would provide the counterpart in this context. Another possibility (5) is offered by a Talmudic passage (Sabbath 116b) that most probably quotes Jesus' very statement in the Aramaic wording: "I have not come to add or take away from the Torah of Moses." This again corresponds exactly to the prescription in Deuteronomy 4:2.

What the evangelist, or his final Greek redactor, may have had in mind when he put an un-Jewish word in Jesus' mouth ("I have come to fulfill [the law and the prophets]") may be indicated by the addition to verse 18, "until everything is fulfilled." This finale leaves open a kind of salvation-history back door that, in complete contradiction to the beginning of the passage, "until heaven and earth pass away," quite candidly envisions a time limit to the jurisdiction of the Torah.

Thus the "fulfillment" of the promises could later be seen in the death and resurrection of Jesus, so that the new era and with it "the end of the law" came with Easter.

This retheologizing was managed through the needle's eye of the Greek word "fulfill," which in Matthew also means to "finish up" something not yet complete (Matt. 23:32) and in Luke (7:1) then becomes to "end."

Paul draws from this the inference that what is "completed" has also "achieved its goal," is therefore concluded, thus can be transcended, and will finally be "terminated."[13]

Thus what Jesus said of the eternal validity of the Torah was, within thirty years, turned into its opposite: Jesus became the "end of the law" (Rom. 10:4). A hundred years later the Gnostic Marcion came within a hair's breadth of eliminating Jesus' entire Bible from the Christian canon.

If Matthew had presented Jesus' phrase in the more precise biblical version cited, even with embellishment, by John of Patmos (Rev. 22:18f.), such an antinomian misrepresentation of this key passage in the Instruction on the Mount would scarcely have been possible.

THE LEAST COMMANDMENT?

In Matthew 5:19 too it can hardly be denied that the Greek redactor has modified the text considerably—"whoever breaks the least commandment." For is there any possibility at all of abolishing any kind of biblical commandment? If not a single letter of the Torah can pass away as long as the world remains, the answer is patent.

It is just as clear that Judaism does indeed recognize "light" and "weighty" commandments ("the weighty matters of the law": Matt. 23:23), but no "least commandment."

Even more unambiguously, Jesus could not have said that "whoever unbinds one of the least of these commandments . . . would be called least" but would nevertheless enter into the realm of heaven, for this would give the lie to the basic tenor of this preamble of the Instruction on the Mount and indirectly encourage violating the Torah. This is all the more true because in the realm of heaven "many who are first will be last, and the last first" (Matt. 19:30).

Jesus almost certainly said that anyone who relaxes only one of the light commandments—such as the tithe on mint, dill, and cumin (Matt. 23:23)—will be found "light" in the reign of God, like that divine judgment on Belshazzar, whose kingdom was "measured . . . weighed and found *too light*" (Dan. 5:25ff.). Here the *tekel* (too light) of the famous Mene-Mene-Tekel-Upharsin passage is a successful wordplay on the "lightest commandment."[14]

Only in this sense of excluding from the realm of heaven those who assume too much freedom in dealing with the Torah would this concluding verse be a fitting finale in the three-part texture of rabbinic rhetoric.

The same ideas were expressed by Rabbi Abba bar Kahana about two hundred fifty years later:

> The Torah has equated the lightest among the commandments and the weightiest. The lightest concerns letting the mother bird go (Deut. 22:6ff.) and the weightiest concerns honoring one's parents (Exod. 20:12); but for both the same [recompense]: so that you may live long! [j Kiddushin I, 61b].

The point is echoed in the Letter of James: "For whoever keeps the whole law but fails in one point has become guilty of all of it" (James 2:10).

RIGHTEOUSNESS

After Jesus in the preamble takes a kind of loyalty oath to his people's book of faith and at the same time rejects any accusation of unscriptural exegesis, the next sentence gives us the programmatic transition from the introduction to the actual content of the Instruction on the Mount:

"For I say to you, unless your righteousness far exceeds that of the scribes and Pharisees, you will not enter into the realm of heaven [Matt. 5:20].

The opening phrase, "for I say to you," indicates a *kelal*, an exegetical key to Jesus' style of scriptural interpretation shared by his predecessors in the exhortation at the entry into the land of Canaan (Deut. 4:1; 6:17f.; 16:20), in the temple liturgy (Pss. 15 and 24), and in the school dialogics of the rabbis.[15]

Matthew, on eleven occasions, stereotypes the scribes and Pharisees as a united front against Jesus. Yet here—important to note— he in no way denies their righteousness, just as elsewhere (23:2f.) he expressly affirms their teaching, though Jesus found it insufficient to meet his moral requirements for entrance into the realm of heaven.

It will be useful to clarify what is translated only inexactly and misleadingly as "righteousness."

By *dikaiosyne*, when it refers to human conduct, is meant "being found correct in God's estimation" or, in Martin Buber's translation, *Bewährung vor Gott*, "qualifying before God." As *sedekah* (the term undoubtedly found in Matthew's Semitic source material) the meaning is more stratified and also includes God's kindness in turning toward humans. This ancient Hebrew word, which defies translation, expresses the two chief attributes of God simultaneously, blending kindness and fairness into a higher unity. For only the harmony of the two corresponds to the Jewish worldview of a righteous Creator and a humanity come of age.

At bottom, *sedekah* corresponds to neither the Greek *dikaiosyne* nor the Roman *justitia*, which is more a juridical category in which debit and credit are balanced so that ethical judgment issues in a judicial correctness that "justifies" humans before God.

What has been lost in translation is the voice of divine love that resonates unmistakably in the prophets' cry for righteousness and in the consciousness that my right, in the framework of *sedakah*, always includes my neighbor's right as well.

When Abraham, disputing with God over Sodom and Gomorrah, ventures to reproach his Creator—"Will you destroy the righteous with the godless? . . . Should the Judge of the entire world not judge righteously?" (Gen. 18:23ff.)—he is thinking neither of jurisdiction nor of judgment, but of this harmony of mercy and love that lies at the core of the Jewish *imitatio Dei*.

Anchored fast in Hebrew belief is the understanding that God is the Righteous—in the Bible, the *Zaddik*—who practices *sedakah* and sets it as an existential task for us as bearers of the divine image. For ultimately the entire spectrum of basic ethical values is contained in righteousness so understood.

Two features characterize this Hebraic *sedakah*: from the Greco-

Roman perspective it is actually unjust in making indebtedness to the needy the touchstone of a lived faith. Indeed, it unites the social with the religious sphere in recognizing "second-class citizens" as those members of the human family who are the special objects of God's solicitude and predilection.

Sedakah thus refers to all our good deeds, from almsgiving to visiting the sick to self-sacrifice for the sake of the neighbor who is our brother or sister under God. Neither broad-mindedness nor patronizing benevolence is involved here, but the fulfillment of a duty—something owed to fellow human beings as their rightful portion of the richness of unmerited gifts with which God showers the world. Such a duty cannot be discharged by mere well-wishing or lip service. Rather it must be performed day after day, always fresh, with a tireless joy in discovery, unwilling to sanction any status quo.

In Judaism the individual as such cannot be or become righteous. Both the vertical component in God the All-Righteous and the horizontal in human fellowship are required, the two complementing and perfecting one another. This social *sedakah*, which can never be complete or absolute, is the Jewish germ cell of holy discontent, the active leaven in human society; ever since Sinai it has allowed no rest but pressed forward with messianic zeal toward the reign of God on earth, when the higher righteousness will finally find its completion. All rabbinic jurisprudence exists only to prepare for this divine dominion.

All this would have been acknowledged by Jesus' opponents, whoever they may have been, under the comprehensive Hebrew term *sedakah*. But Jesus impresses on his disciples that their *sedakah* must be measurably increased, which at first seems to suggest a quantitative increase in fulfillment of the Torah. But because any measure of Jewish "righteousness" presupposes absolute loyalty to the Torah, what is meant here can be only a *qualitatively* better righteousness, a concept common in rabbinic scriptural interpretation.

To bring home to ourselves its full significance for believing Jews, let us go back to the generation after Jesus. Why was Jerusalem destroyed? This is the fateful question that the Sages in Israel found themselves forced to face after that national catastrophe of the year 70. They answered with a chorus of confessions of sin the like of which for brutal self-criticism is unknown in all the literature of religion. Better to be destitute, to suffer and hunger—we read between the lines from those years of dejection—than live with an unjust God. Pivotal among the many answers was that of Rabbi Johanan: "Jerusalem has been destroyed only because [the judges] judged there according to the norm of Torah legislation" (Baba Metzia 30b).

To the amazed counterquestion of his colleagues as to where the judges had failed, he explained, "They administered justice precisely according to the demands of the Torah—instead of remaining inside the legal line."

The last phrase is a virtually untranslatable Hebraism that the evangelist has tried to render with "(instead of) the better righteousness" (Matt. 5:20). This concept expresses a search for the in-depth meaning of law and righteousness that generates the courage to think the commandment of love of neighbor through to its ultimate consequences.

To speak concretely—and the rabbis always thought in concrete terms—it is a matter of the spiritual elite imposing on themselves a more stringent application of the commandment, of voluntarily waiving a right for the sake of resolving a conflict, of disobeying the (Roman) command to hate one's (anti-Roman) neighbor, of fulfillment beyond all the social rules in order to serve and protect others and give flexibility priority in all controversy.

In short: a theo-politics of small steps, whose common goal it is to satisfy the command in Deuteronomy 6:18: "Do what is *right and good* in the eyes of the Lord." Here the *doing* of the good gives horizontal justice its vertical dimension.

In the melancholy contemplation of that catastrophe of the year 70 it was the lack of this "better" righteousness that was held responsible for the destruction of Jerusalem. It was the fullness of this same altruistic uprightness that Jesus, a generation earlier, taught was the way to prepare for the heavenly Jerusalem.

If Jesus' strategy for the realm of heaven lay in the radical actualization of the commandment of love, his salvation tactic was to be found in the "better righteousness" that would eliminate interpersonal hostility from the world. This messianic program for true humanization—in the sense of becoming worthy bearers of the divine image—is then explained with the help of the six so-called antitheses in Matthew 5:21–48 (part three of this book).

What may have roused Jesus to this promising alternative to human self-destruction is an early rabbinic debate on the wording of the commandment of love of neighbor: "Love your neighbor as yourself!" (Lev. 19:18). Yes, but can love ever be commanded? Hardly! But let us read more exactly. The verb is not the imperative, but the future form; "You *will* love your neighbor as yourself."

When will that happen? When God plants the Torah in our heart and writes it in our mind (Jer. 31:33), when God "removes the heart of stone and gives us a heart of flesh" (Ezek. 26:26), then we will no longer need commandments and rules to make us understand that love of neighbor is the overflow of love of God. It will not be an external force that will then impel us to love, but an internal urge— a drive to devote ourselves to the brothers and sisters whom God has given us and whom we need in order to become mature and adult in our self-realization.

This eschatological "transcription" of all the commandments of love—of protection of the married woman, reconciliation with one's brother or sister, unlimited forgiveness extending even to love of enemy—from the stone tables of Sinai to human hearts is the core of Jesus' Instruction on the Mount.

Part II

THE BEATITUDES

Chapter 3

INSTRUCTION FOUNDED ON LOVE (Matt. 5:3–12)

Between the introduction and the "antitheses" of the Instruction on the Mount we find a series of axioms, which, because of their repetition of the initial word "happy"—*beatus* in Latin—have been named the Beatitudes. Neither lesson nor lecture, they are Jesus' concrete response to the needs of the people, springing from his unshakable faith in the promises given to Israel.

The rabbi from Nazareth obviously took Isaiah's proclamation as a personal commission to be fulfilled here and now, and again and again: "Strengthen the tired hands and revive the stumbling knees. Say to the despairing hearts: Be of good cheer. Do not be afraid. See, your God is coming" (Isa. 35:3–4).

TO THE POOR, THE REALM OF HEAVEN

The courage Jesus inspires here in his followers is an essential prerequisite for his program of action that follows, for unless power is awarded to the powerless, hope to the despairing, and light to those who dwell on the shadow side of life, no effective collaboration in the saving of this world can be expected.

To those suffering from hunger, to the destitute, and the marginal members of Jewish society who suffer day after day from the futility of all their exertions, hope is here given that, despite all appearances to the contrary, all the suffering and struggling will turn out to be meaningful. God's plan of salvation for humans is far from coming to an end; God is the Ruler of the world, the God of the lowly, dwelling among the poor and the repentant (Isa. 57:15).

The realm of God is near! Help it to break through, the message rings out confidently, by remaining loyal to God and God's world! These Beatitudes offer neither congratulations nor consolation with promises for the *next* world; they are the good news that the God of our forebears, who demands a reversal of our own thinking, will reassess all earthly values here below.

Out of tears will come laughter, out of hunger satiety, out of sadness consolation, and out of hate will grow salvation—in short: the realm of heaven is near *if* you will it.

But what is the significance of this shorthand transcript of the hopes inherent in rabbinic teaching on God? The Greek text of Matthew is a literal rendering from Jesus' mother tongue: "the realm of the heavens." In Hebrew "heaven" is a plural form; there is no singular. The phrase is one of the numerous descriptive terms for God—the Most-Praised, the Lord, his Name, our Father in Heaven, the Merciful—all synonymous, which Jesus, like all pious Jews, used in order to avoid desecrating the holy by inordinate repetition.

"The realm of heaven," then, is not to be found in the heavens; the phrase refers to God's absolute and manifest dominion on this earth, the possession of which is awarded to the gentle—or, better, the powerless—in the third Beatitude. The "Old Song of Renunciation, the *Eiapopeia* from Heaven," which Heinrich Heine in his *Wintermärchen* puts into the mouth of a maiden with a harp, is not a "new song" at all but, in its thought, part of the rabbinic teachings of more than two thousand years:

> I know the style, I know the text,
> I know the gentlemen who write.
> I know they secretly drank wine
> And publicly preached water.
> A new song, a better song,
> I will compose for you, my friends.
> Here on this earth we shall already
> Build the realm of heaven.

The last two lines would have evoked hardly any protest from Jesus, although he might have replaced "build" with "prepare."

But it is also not a "realm" in the usual sense of the word, which implies both temporal and geographical limitations; it is rather the emergence of God's royal dominion over all creation—a dominion that of course has existed in the hidden depths since the beginning of the world, but is capturing human hearts only little by little, mysteriously, not abruptly or forcefully. It will free the world from discord, isolation, and bondage, make it habitable for trust, harmony, and peace.

But for Jesus' contemporaries a political component must also have resonated in the concept of heaven. In more than a dozen proverbs and figures of speech of that time "Roman realm" and "heavenly realm" are paired as irreconcilable contrasts in which force and gentleness, war and peace, brutality and righteousness, hate and love are embodied most unambiguously.

Good news, redemption, and the realm of heaven—these three foundations of Jesus' salvation vocabulary were thus then, as also today, charged with theo-political dynamite for every attentive listener.

What Nietzsche wrote of a "slave revolt in morality" was not completely wrong:

It was the Jews who, with awe-inspiring consistency, dared to invert the aristocratic value-equation (good = noble = powerful = beautiful = happy = beloved of God), . . . saying "the wretched alone are the good; the poor, impotent, lowly alone are the good; the suffering deprived, sick, ugly alone are pious, alone are blessed by God, blessedness is for them alone. . . ."[16]

HAPPY

We find the word "happy" at the beginning of both the Psalter and the series of nine Beatitudes, which remind us again and again of the psalms; perhaps they are *intended* to remind us, for the psalms are part of the daily liturgy of the synagogue in which Jesus tirelessly preached his message.

"Happy the one who does not walk in the counsel of the godless" (Ps.1:1).

"Happy the one who cares for the weak" (Ps. 41:1).

"Happy those who keep the commandments and do justice at all times" (Ps. 106:3).

"Happy the one who is charitable and gladly lends and conducts his affairs as is just" (Ps. 112:5).

"Happy those who live without blame, who walk in the law of the Lord" (Ps. 119:1).

Sometimes the similarity extends to the contents as well:

Happy are the grieving, for they will be consoled [Matt. 5:4].

This would remind biblically-oriented Jews at once that "the Lord is near to those whose heart is bruised, and he helps those whose spirit is crushed" (Ps. 34:19), and also that "those who sow in tears will reap in joy" (Ps. 126:5).

Happy are the pure in heart, for they will see God [Matt. 5:8].

This, the sixth Beatitude, is similar in meaning to "Who will ascend the mountain of the Lord? And who has innocent hands and is of pure heart?" (Ps. 24:4).

Happy are the gentle, for they will inherit the land of Israel [Matt. 5:5].

This tangible, three-dimensional promise is also held out in Psalm 37:11.

How to translate the key initial word with an equivalent that will do justice to the meaning intended by both the psalmist and the teacher on the mount is a question with which Martin Buber struggled hard in his translation of the Psalter. Certainly the Hebrew *ashre* is translated only feebly by the Greek *makarios* or the Latin *beatus*, and only imprecisely by the German *wohl* or *heil*. The French *bienheureux*, like the English "blessed," is also not very helpful. Quite surprisingly, the "happy" of the *New American Bible* seems to come closest to the original sense.

Let us listen to what Buber says in his introduction to the Psalter:

The psalmist cries, "Oh, how fortunate the man. . . . " This
is not a wish or a promise; it is not that the man in question
earns good fortune or is certain of becoming fortunate,
either still in this earthly life or in another, future life. This is a
joyful cry and an enthusiastic declaration: How fortunate
indeed is this man! In the cry, timeless by its nature, the
division of now and later, of earthly and future life is virtually
absorbed. . . . The psalmist obviously wishes to say, "Pay
attention, for there is a secret good fortune, hidden by the
hands of life itself, which counterbalances and outbalances
all misfortune. You do not see it, but it is the true, indeed the
only good fortune."

THIRST FOR ACTION

Three linguistic peculiarities help us plumb the depths of these
nine happinesses. First, they are formulated in the indicative mode
of fact, not in the imperative mode of the moral sermon, and yet
the inner certainty of salvation that they disclose must arouse a
devout thirst for action when sown in Jewish hearts.

"We will *do* all that the Lord has said," says all Israel in the wake
of its central experience of God at Mt. Sinai (Exod. 19:8). The echo
reverberates from the Instruction on the Mount: "Not everyone
who says to me 'Lord, Lord' will enter the realm of heaven, but
only the one who *does* the will of my Father" (Matt. 7:21).

The knowledge of being borne along, of being led, kindles in
hearts a fire of happiness that cannot sit still, cannot find fulfillment even in prayer. It seeks expression in the great joy of being
allowed to serve God and to further God's ardently longed-for
lordship by even a single inch. It is not achievements but service to
God's reign that matters, not work but above all love. Yet for Jews
love of God without deeds pleasing to God is hypocrisy, empty
blather. In Jesus' words, "By their fruits you will know them!"
(Matt. 7:16).

The second linguistic characteristic is that, although those called
happy are the active endurers, the grieving, the nonviolent, the
merciful, and the peacemakers, the happiness brought about in
them is expressed in a *passivum divinum*. They are comforted (i.e.,
it is not that they comfort themselves), filled, and called offspring

of God. They are "mercied," as the Hebrew puts it, using this pious construction to make it clear that God is the author of their good fortune. Again and again it is God, in all nine Beatitudes.

Two insights silently mesh here. "We are God's collaborators" (1 Cor. 3:9), as Paul emphasizes in good rabbinic fashion—collaborators who, if we "love not with the tongue but in works and truth" (1 John 3:18), may count on God's love in return. The second insight flows from the explanation of a psalm verse that Jesus certainly knew, "One thing I ask of the Lord; for that I strive" (Ps. 27:4). This passage is not to be seen as a superfluous repetition but as a two-part assertion joining deed to prayer to prove itself worthy of being heard. Jews do not believe they can earn God's grace through pious works, but a few rabbis are of the opinion that one can perhaps attain it in humility and works of charity.

A third peculiarity of language lies in the fact that, with the exception of the first and last Beatitudes, all are grammatically in the future. The two present-tense verbs refer to the realm of heaven; the original Aramaic here certainly used the ancient wording, "They have a share in the world to come," so that they too give priority to the future, even if a foretaste of it can already be sensed today.

Clearly this approaching splendor, the divine future, ought to inspire a radical alteration of the present, but the change is always yet to come. *Now* the poor are still poor, the persecuted continue to be slandered, and God has not yet wiped away the tears of the sorrowing, as Isaiah, like John of Patmos, promises.

This hard reality, though neither whitewashed nor glossed over in dead silence, is modified by the fact of the awaited redemption, which for the faithful is a reality for the morrow. Because ultimately and finally faith is "a conviction of things unseen" (Heb. 11:1). And "hope that is seen to be already fulfilled is not hope, for how can one hope for something that one sees?" (Rom 8:24).

Intensely aware of the inadequacy of all temporality, Jesus looks back to the Sinai of the law so that, inspired by the divine revelation given so long ago and never forgotten, he can direct his gaze ahead to the future vision of Israel's prophets, when divine law and righteousness will bring peace to humankind.

In the tensed spanning of this bipolar vision, today disappears for him into the eye of the needle through which the thread of memory tirelessly continues to weave the stuff of the future. That is why the poor and the grieving, the gentle, the merciful, and the persecuted are even *now* to be called happy, for they are assured of their share in the coming heavenly kingdom.

There is no postponing to the next world, no shrinking to the interior spiritual life here, because for Jesus, like the prophets before him, it is the whole that matters. He is really speaking of the poor who will experience the realm of heaven; true peace will come between individuals, classes, and peoples; force will really yield to love—because all will learn in their hearts what best serves their own and others' welfare. And good fortune will reign in concord and fellowship on this earth, which God called "very good" (Gen. 1:31). This is the mustard seed of hope in a curable world that Jesus here sows in the mother soil of biblical promises.

In this sense the Beatitudes also contain a gentle but firm protest against two opposing radicalisms of Jesus' day, both of which tried to bestow a divine blessing on violence: the Zealots struggling against the pagan yoke, and hoping to defeat the Roman forces by a kind of holy war, and the imperial Roman authority claiming to be a "pacifier" and "bearer of salvation" in order to crown the dictated peace of the *pax romana* with the halo of divine approbation.

Between the lived present and the awaited future there is a fertile borderland where the Beatitudes are set as an earnest for a redemption worthy of belief and as an incentive for a vigorous yearning for a salvation that does not simply fall from heaven. In human affairs, there is first of all a contract or commitment, then performance, and finally payment. With God it is exactly the other way around: the gift comes first, then the commitment or obligation it inspires, and then, with unparalleled patience, God waits for human performance.

SHALOM

The clearest intimation that this salvation is not merely to be requested but must also, according to God's decree, be prepared for, is found in the seventh Beatitude, which Martin Luther translated as "Happy are the peace-loving, for they shall be called the children of God" (Matt. 5:9).

I find the translation "peaceloving" (Luther's *friedfertig* literally means "peace-ready") insufficient, for it signifies a readiness of an almost passive nature, a consent to peace, without any urge toward action, whereas Jesus had in mind a vigorous working for peace, which amounts to doing the will of God.

Nor are those who voluntarily take this duty upon themselves "children," as Luther imprecisely renders it, but mature, adult sons and daughters who, though always dependent on their Father, are nevertheless mature in their piety and responsible for their actions.

The mistranslation "children" frequently used by Luther (apparently in order not to diminish the uniqueness of Jesus' sonship) can be an enticement to powerlessness, to seeking childlike security in the lap of the sort of maternal God whose chief function seems to be helping, consoling, protecting. A belated cutting of such an umbilical cord is needed in struggling to be independent sons and daughters of God who, even amid tensions and frictions, collaborate in the building of peace.

Even in this key concept, "peace," the Greek text misleads us into too narrow a meaning. For shalom corresponds neither to the *eirene* or "not-war" of the Greeks, nor to the *pax* or "coordination power" of the Romans. It means primarily an integral wholeness, the antithesis of all schizophrenia and division.

The wholeness is three-dimensional, reflecting a unique, God-willed harmony (Ps. 85:9): directed within, it is purity of heart (Lam. 3:17); directed above, it is being at one with God (Judg. 6:24); and directed to all sides it is human unity (1 Kings 5:4).

In the biblical understanding of wholeness, the political, social, and religious are no more to be separated from one another than are body and soul, or nature and culture.

Thus welfare and salvation, well-being, peace of mind, good fortune, and social harmony are the mutually complementary components of one and the same shalom, itself as indivisible as the biblical oneness of politics, society, nature, and theology— all parts of a single world order under the one Creator God. In the words of the German bishops in their "Declaration on the Relationship of the Church to Judaism" of March 28, 1980:

Christians and Jews together can and should advocate what in Hebrew is called *shalom*. This is a comprehensive concept that signifies peace, joy, freedom, reconciliation, community, harmony, righteousness, truth, communication, humanity [p. 27].

THE THEO-POLITICS OF SMALL STEPS

According to the rabbis, "All commandments are to be fulfilled when the right opportunity arrives. But not peace! Peace you must seek out and pursue!" This pursuit of peace commanded by the psalmist (Ps. 34:14) is also referred to as to "make peace" (Isa. 27:5; Josh. 9:15), as Jesus puts it here in rather flat Greek but impeccable Hebrew. This is a creative making, as when God "made" the sun, moon, and stars (Gen. 1:16). For this reason one of the most frequent synonyms for God in the synagogue liturgy is "the Pacifier" or, more precisely, "the Peacemaker," because dismantling the walls of mistrust and building bridges takes great effort. I am speaking here of persuasion, a tactful bringing-together, seeking out subtle possibilities for compromise such as those modeled for us by God in the aphoristic rabbinical material that encourages us to an *imitatio Dei*. Even in Jesus' lifetime the Talmudic fathers, faced with the question of whether peace on earth is at all achievable, answer with a theo-politics of small steps: curtailing conflicts, blunting confrontations, waiving rights, keeping and going beyond the law of love, being flexible, and all the thousand and one ways of persistent "busy-bee" labor "for the sake of peace," as the Talmud so often says. This is to be a human collaboration in the plan of salvation whose goal remains not merely an absence of conflict but the full being-at-peace of the world under God.

Just how human peace tactics relate to the plenary divine reconciliation of shalom is illuminated by a rabbinic parable that recommends the cooking pot as a model for all peacemakers. The lowly cooking pot, without any fanfare, performs a daily miracle that ought to inspire even politicians. As its thin bottom separates the two inimical elements of fire and water from one another, it does not reconcile the two of them but succeeds in inducing them to peaceful and constructive collaboration. A culinary cooperation from which flows good in the form of tasty blessings—no mean accomplishment in any epoch of our lacerated human history!

No less realistic in his peace efforts was the prophet Isaiah, who called on his hearers to "beat their swords into plowshares and their spears into sickles" (Isa. 2:4)—in his day neither a flowery figure of speech nor poetic effusiveness, but a plain everyday possibility. In those days of the late iron age, farmers fastened an iron spike to a wooden plow to cultivate their fields. But in times of war they fastened that same piece of iron to a shaft that could then serve as a weapon.

Isaiah, Jesus, and the rabbis never hide the reality of war, and no utopian "Embrace one another, ye millions" issues from their mouths. But they do soberly draw attention to the possibility of an international equalization before God—"God will judge among the peoples"—for which this symbolic reforging of all swords into tools of peaceful bread-winning could smooth the way. Only when earthly peacemakers have brought enemies close together in such a fashion and move them to collaboration in God's saving work, will God perfect this initial human pacification by the irresistible attraction of divine love, making friends of David and Goliath, Israel and Edom, fire and water, as one of the eschatological anecdotes of the Talmud puts it.

THE HIGHEST COMMANDMENT

I used to think that the Beatitudes should stand at the end of the Instruction on the Mount, as its climax, closing it with the crowning promise, "Rejoice and be glad, for your reward will be great in the realm of heaven!" (Matt. 5:12). One day as I was reading the Ten Commandments a new insight dawned on me.

"I am the Lord your God who brought you out of Egypt, out of slavery" (Exod. 20:2) begins the decalogue—not with a command but with a declaration of fact: liberating proof of God's love. It alone, say the rabbis, gives God the right to address human beings by their first names and to expect them to take up the yoke of the heavenly realm, as Jews like to call the voluntary assumption of the burden of the commandments.

In the same way the Instruction on the Mount begins with the Beatitudes. All nine give eloquent evidence of that same divine love, directed not simply toward humanity in general but especially toward the victims of human unkindness, the disadvantaged, those who always come in last, who especially need comfort and affection.

It is only this reality of God's compassionate turning to us that gives God the right, so to speak, to expect the same from us, a charity no less magnanimous toward all our fellow humans, our sisters and brothers under God. Such a love signals the end of resentment, vengeance, cursing, adultery, retaliation, and all alienation and animosity. What are all the imperatives of the Instruction on the Mount if not a concerted call to absolute fulfillment of the Torah in its original meaning, the concrete teaching of the all-encompassing love of God and love of neighbor? These two loves are inseparably linked together by the commandment of sanctification, "Be holy, for I, the Lord your God, am holy!" as we read in the nineteenth chapter of Leviticus, at the center of the five books of Moses—and the center of all scripture, according to the rabbis.

This unmistakable call to the imitation of God was considered an unforgivable blasphemy in Greece and Rome, but in Judaism it is understood as the highest of all commandments.

Four things, then, are contained in these Beatitudes: a kind of "empowerment," that of the first commandment, for the moral demands that follow; encouragement at a time of need; a theological declaration that God is to be understood as lover of the lowly; and a theopsychological truism— that not "whoever believes *will be* happy" (Mark 16:16), but that whoever believes, sincerely and unshakably, *is* already happy.

Part III

"AND I SAY TO YOU"
(Matt. 5:21–48)

Chapter 4

ABROGATION OF THE LAW?

Even today some Christian theologians find it difficult to reconcile their faith with the historical facts that during his life the founder of the Christian church belonged to another religion, that he honored the Torah as the imperishable substance of revelation, and considered only his own Israel to be the people of God to whom he devoted his entire life and endeavors on earth.

One popular solution is to dejudaize Jesus spiritually, at the same time disparaging his Bible and his primitive Jewish church. In her collection *Anti-Judaism in Christian Theology*, Charlotte Klein, a Catholic nun, cites thirty-seven well-known Catholic and Protestant theologians who condemn "the law."[17] Joachim Jeremias says it "contradicts the commandment of God" (Klein, 41). Günther Schiwy says this "Mosaic religion . . . rests on a culpable misunderstanding, an insistence on the 'old' law, and for two thousand years it has been on a wrong track through its own fault" (ibid., 48).

According to Romano Guardini, Judaism deals in hypocrisy: "on the outside, greatest delicacy of conscience; on the inside, hardness of heart. Outer loyalty to the Law; inner sin" (ibid., 50).

Heinrich Schlier says "the law has become a trap for the Jews and they are caught in it." The Jews at bottom do not seek God "but themselves," so that "contrary to their own knowledge and striving, they hate God" (ibid., 52).

In Judaism, writes Günther Bornkamm, it is through the works required by the law that "the great reckoning with God begins:

41

reckoning and counter-reckoning; merit and debt; reward and punishment; the actions of men being bartered in transaction with God" (ibid., 56).

The legalistic piety of the Jews is, in the opinion of Adolph Schlatter, "mere appearance, and the desires for which they struggled were exclusively selfish: they were fighting for money and women" (ibid., 61).

Charlotte Klein sums up:

> In Judaism oppressive burdens, in the gospel liberating grace. None of these theologians can get rid of this wrong conception. . . . Behind this biased judgment lie ignorance of Judaism as it really is and arbitrary interpretation of the texts [ibid., 53].

Most authors make use of the Instruction on the Mount to "prove" that Jesus wished to "burst" or "transcend" the Judaism of his birth, that he wished to "abolish" or "relativize" or even "reject" the Torah. Dietrich von Oppen, for example, writes, "The contents of the Sermon on the Mount are the vanquishing of the law, i.e., of the strict, institutionally-composed, Jewish public order."[18]

In Joseph Ruppert Geiselmann we read, "Jesus claims an authority which stands alongside that of Moses, indeed rises above it. This has no equal on Jewish soil."[19]

Ethelbert Stauffer outdoes most of his colleagues when he asserts that the Sermon on the Mount is "a demonstration against Moses," which makes Jesus, "in the eyes of Torah Jews, . . . an apostate of an unsympathetic sort. But Jesus is more than an apostate, he is a seducer and even more—he is a preacher of dissidence."[20]

We are left amazed, speechless. How can a pious Jew, who is given the title rabbi fourteen times in the Gospels, who gathered hundreds of disciples around him and preached innumerable times in the synagogues of his Galilean homeland, become an alleged destroyer of the Torah that was the sole Bible for him and his, which he referred to continually, which never left his mouth, and whose abiding holiness he was so careful to emphasize? Is not a rabbi who "abolishes" his Torah just as unthinkable as a Jesuit who denounces the papacy or a Lutheran bishop who condemns Martin Luther?

Did not Jesus himself, after he had compared the least details in the Torah (the tithing of mint, dill, and cumin) with the "weightier matters of the law" (righteousness, mercy, and faithfulness), say, "The one ought to be done and the other not neglected" (Matt. 23:23)? And to all those who call him "Lord, Lord" but do not adhere to the divine instruction, he will say on the day of the Final Judgment, "Go away from me, you who do what is contrary to the Torah" (Matt. 7:23). Did not Paul also say of his Savior that he "was put under the law" (Gal. 4:4) and was throughout his life "a servant of the circumcision" (Rom. 15:8)—a Hebrew way to stress his unconditional loyalty to the Torah?

This fact has also been acknowledged by the French Bishops' Conference in its declaration." "The Attitude of Christians to Judaism" (April 16, 1973): "It must not be forgotten that Jesus, born a Jew . . . fulfilled his task within the framework of the people of the covenant by his obedience to the Torah and by his prayer."

To invalidate all this evidence, the antinomians cling to four Greek words that occur five times in the Instruction on the Mount: *ego de lego hymin*, "but I say to you."

An invitation sent to me by a Catholic academy to attend a conference on the Sermon on the Mount commented:

> With these words Jesus revolutionized the legalistic religion of Judaism in his time. Here lies the beginning of the liberating message of the New Testament, which has nothing in common with the anxieties and pressures of a legalistic and formalistic religion.

In these four Greek words lies a "completely unique claim to authority" (Karl Barth); an "unequalled sovereign fullness of power" (Kurt Niederwimmer); indeed, something "completely unheard of in Judaism" (Michael Schmaus), which "has no parallel in rabbinism" (Georg Eichholz)—to cite only four typical statements of Christian scholars. All these statements testify at best to gaps in their knowledge of Jesus' mother tongue and his *Sitz im Leben*, shortcomings that specialists in English or German literature, for example, could never permit themselves in the study of Shakespeare or Goethe.

JESUS' MOTHER TONGUE

On the linguistic side let it first be emphasized that, "*but* I say to you" focuses attention on a contrast that the Greek wording does not justify. In the gospel text the little word *de* generally designates a coupling, "and," not an opposition, "but."

An accurate translation would read, "*And* I say to you," corresponding exactly to the original Hebrew wording, which is never used to introduce a contradiction to the Torah, but rather the opposite, its elucidation: *va ani omer lachem.*

Far from being "unique," it is a scholarly concept of the "oral Torah" tradition and has its parallels in Talmudic writings. "You have heard" or "It is said," followed by "And I say to you" are a complementary pair of technical expressions from the basic vocabulary of rabbinic rhetoric.[21] The first means, "Until now you have understood this scriptural passage in the following way," whereupon either the literal sense, the current exegesis, or the opinion of one's opponent is quoted. Then follows the second phrase, "And I say to you," presenting the proponent's new explanation.

A similar opinion is advanced by Lutheran Bishop Eduard Lohse in his essay, "Ich aber sage euch," in the *Festschrift für Joachim Jeremias* (Göttingen, 1970), where he cites, among other sources, Rabbi Simeon ben Johai, who contradicted the argumentation of Rabbi Akiba five times with an emphatic "And I say to you." Lohse writes:

> When Jesus opposes his words to the general customary explanation of the commandment with the phrase *ego de lego hymin*, this usage is quite comparable to the expression used by the rabbis, *va ani omer lachem*, for in both cases an opinion is brought forward that departs from the general customary understanding [Lohse, 196].

Anyone reading Jesus' debate dialogues with the eyes of a knowledgeable Talmudist knows that, without exception, they are examples of the passionate teaching dialects used by the rabbis, a method arising not from enmity or know-it-all dogmatism, but solely from the shared love of holy writ, the struggle to expound it in a fashion most pleasing to God, and the knowledge that monologue is the worst way and dialogue the best for brothers to get closer to a truth that is hidden. Neither in the debate dialogues nor in the Instruction on the Mount did Jesus ever abandon the ground of his pluralistic Judaism. Like all the luminaries of Israel up to the present day, he *had* to evoke contradiction, for his contribution to his people's deposit of faith was that of a constructive, tension-filled contrast/harmony, in which both elements underline his unyielding Jewishness. *Harmony* in all principles and foundations of faith—as in the twofold commandment of love (Mark 12:28ff.) and the imperishability of the Torah (Matt. 5:17ff.)—is complemented by legitimate *contrast* in numerous details, such as healing on the Sabbath, the tax question, and washing of hands, as well as in the focus of his understanding of scripture and the practical consequences that he drew from his acute messianic expectations.

All in all, a plurality of insights into faith and religious practices could not but enrich the store of Israel's teachings, especially important two thousand years ago when the "oral Torah" was at the point of being crystalized in a dialectical-dialogical manner into normative halakah.

"And I say to you" must therefore be read against the background of the "Sayings of the Fathers," in which we read, "It is true of any dispute carried on for the sake of heaven that it ultimately leads to something permanent. . . . What would be an example of such a dispute? that between Hillel and Shammai"(Aboth V, 20). What is referred to here is the dispute between the two main schools of the Pharisees, whose views often reverberate in Jesus' sayings.

NOT EVEN ONE ANTITHESIS

The moat between Jesus and his adversaries is artificially deepened by reference to the six so-called antitheses, which represent the ethical framework of the Instruction on the Mount. With the best of will, however, I am unable to discover in the Instruction on the Mount even a single antithesis in the sense of a counterclaim that would contradict a previously stated thesis.

When Jesus says, "You have heard . . . you should not kill" (Matt. 5:21), an antithesis would run, "but I say to you, do away with anyone who stands in your way."

When Jesus quotes the biblical thesis, "You have heard you should not commit adultery" (Matt. 5:27), the corresponding antithesis would be found in something like Adolf Hitler's attitude:

> This stupid "thou shalt not"! It must be eliminated from our blood, this curse from Mount Sinai! This poison with which both Jews and Christians have spoiled and defiled the free, wonderful instincts of humans and reduced them to the level of fawning fear . . . ! What we are battling is the so-called Law![22]

Jesus furnishes us, thank God, not with antitheses but with "supertheses," which deepen, intensify, and radicalize the biblical commandments—guiding us back to their roots and original intention. In Martin Buber's words, "Sinai is not enough for him. He seeks the clouds above the mountain from which the voice comes; he would penetrate God's original intent . . . in order to fulfill the Torah—that is, to invoke and actualize its fullness."

In this idealistic yearning for perfection, Jesus calls upon his hearers to go beyond fulfillment of commands and prohibitions, in line with the tenth commandment, which goes beyond all the others in warning for the first time of evil desires, even before they ripen into wrongdoing: "You shall not covet your neighbor's house . . . nor his wife nor his manservant nor his womanservant nor his ox nor his donkey nor anything that belongs to your neighbor" (Exod. 20:17).

INTENT AND DEED

Here—at the point where the decalogue ends in the wilderness, among primitive nomads and runaway slaves, with its ethical peak at Israel's dawn—the Instruction on the Mount resumes. In the framework of a divine pedagogy seen not as fixed once and for all, but capable of advance, it strives to eliminate the difference between evil intent and the wrongdoing arising from it.

Not only murder but even anger is condemned; not only adultery but even a lewd glance is illicit; not only perjury but any oath is evil; not only peaceableness but also humility and renunciation of rights are building blocks of the shalom of the future. Such a Torah exegesis could be described as theocentric or "perfectionistic," but in good rabbinic fashion it is also based on the insight that the way to sin is like the stepladder described in an old explanation of Genesis 6:5: "Sinful imagination leads to desire; desire to intent; intent to pursuit; pursuit to deed. This is to have you know how difficult it is for a person to turn back from one to the other" (Kalla Rabbati II, 6). If, then, desire "is the beginning of all sin," as the Apocalypse of Moses (§ 19) says, "desire conceives and gives birth to sin," as the letter of James says, "but sin gives birth to death" (1:15).

From this realistic perception it is but a short step to the conclusion, "Resist the beginnings," which is the leitmotif of Jesus' "supertheses."

The Hebrew word for "desire" can also be translated into German as *Neid* (envy), coming from the primitive form *nit*, which has the meaning of "to feud, to overcome, to criticize severely." Such desire, as old as Cain's wrath against his brother Abel, leads to displeasure, to jealousy, to wrangling; ultimately it can destroy the basis of human coexistence.

This insidious sin "crouches outside the door" and hungers for you" (Gen. 4:7), as God warns Cain, "but you will be master over it!"

Such mastery over one's own sinful desires is what moralists call "the holy no": composure in saying no to all seductions that run contrary to one's ethos. It is bought dearly, through sacrifice graphically described by Jesus as "plucking out your eye" and "cutting off your hand"; these two, the gateway and servant of sin, must be curbed and controlled, even, as it were, by a readiness to suffer loss of limb (Matt. 5:29–30).

Admission into the realm of God is not to be had on less stringent terms. It entails a new form of community, prepared and determined to live without hate or anger in a fellowship that goes far beyond the demands of mere justice. For its sake Jesus renounces all family bonds, for "whoever does the will of God is my brother, sister and mother" (Mark 3:35). But "to do the will of God" means to found an "ideal kibbutz" as the abode of faith, taking God's affection for humans seriously enough to model interhuman relationships on it.

Such a demanding ethos for the people of God, based on this teaching of the "supertheses," has always provoked three completely different reactions.

"He is out of his mind!" say Jesus' relatives, who write him off as a crackpot and visionary (Mark 3:21).

"You are the salt of the earth . . ., the light of the world . . ., a city on a mountain" (Matt. 5:13–16). In this way Jesus won the hearts of his disciples, an advance guard exemplifying the power and feasibility of his vision to others.

The third reaction is detached and deprecatory, assigning this concrete revolutionary program to the rosy cloud world of noncommital utopia.

To discover where and how far Jesus' "supertheses" deviate from rabbinic instruction, or even contradict the commandments of the Torah, they will have to be discussed individually.

Chapter 5

MURDER
(Matt. 5:21–24)

Jesus begins his protest against inhumanity with the most malicious and oldest sin against God's creative kindness. The first human who had a brother struck him dead. Fratricide—and in the Bible all forms of murder are fratricide (Gen. 9:5f.)—has still today not ceased to make us seriously question the integrity of human nature.

You have heard that it was said to the ancients, "You should not kill [Exod. 20:13], but anyone who (nevertheless) kills should be subject to the death penalty" [Exod. 21:12].
And I say to you, anyone who is angry with a brother shall be subject to the death penalty. For whoever calls a brother "blockhead" is subject to the Sanhedrin; but anyone who says "(godless) fool" will be subject to hellfire [Matt. 5:21–22].

One is struck at once by the typical rabbinic three-pronged escalation that lists increasingly more serious injuries to one's brother, though stopping short of violating the words of the Torah. The angry thought in the heart should be taken before the city council; a public insult should be brought before the high council; a flagrant defamation is so grave that only the divine court is in a position to punish it.

"You should not kill" says the decalogue (Exod. 20:13). We all know from experience that homicide begins in the heart with hate

49

for or disparagement of someone as a "misanthrope," a "parasite," or "vermin." It develops from the demon that creates ideologies or theories for itself in which the other is brutally relegated to categories like "inhuman" or "subhuman." It can begin at a desk or be drafted in an office. Because every murder begins in the heart, it is there that it must be nipped in the bud.

For this reason Jesus makes use of the old rabbinic principle of the "hedge around the Torah," the intensified precautionary prescriptions laid down as a protection against any transgression of the commandments and prohibitions. In the words of the "Sayings of the Fathers," "The oral tradition is a hedge for the Torah; vows are a hedge for continence; silence is a hedge for wisdom"(Aboth III, 13).

Whether the obscure Greek wording of the first "superthesis" does in fact give expression to an escalating triad depends largely on the word *more* (Matt. 5:22), which permits of three translations. If it is a Greek vocative, then "fool" is meant; in Hebrew the word could mean "insurrectionist"; but in Aramaic it would be "apostate" or "blasphemer," probably the acme of calumny.

In any case, the meaning is, "Let everyone be ready to listen but restrained in speech and slow to anger," as it says in the Letter of James, "for in anger one does not do what is righteous before God" (1:19f.). To put it another way: though anger does not, of course, take the lives of others, it destroys solidarity with them, and robs them of both their dignity and a measure of their humanity. German speaks of *Rufmord*, English of "character assassination."

The same idea can be seen in the rabbinic saying, "Whoever hates a neighbor [i.e., performs malicious deeds] is counted among those who shed blood" (Derech Erez Rabba 11).

The Talmud makes the connection between shaming and killing even clearer:

A teacher of Mishna taught before Rav Nahman, son of Isaac: "If anyone makes the face of a companion pale before a crowd, it is as if he shed blood." He said to him: "That is excellently stated. (It can be noticed in an ashamed person as in a dying person how the color recedes and the person becomes pale.) I have seen how the redness vanishes and the pallor comes" [BM 58b].

The same is true of the flush of shame, which can be interpreted as an inner shedding of blood.

There is thus something of an anatomical indication that those who make their neighbor pale or flush burden themselves with blood guilt.

The moral of the following Talmudic excerpt goes even further in saying, "Die rather than humiliate someone":

Rabbi Johanan said in the name of Rabbi Simeon, son of Johai: It is better to let oneself fall into a fiery furnace than make a companion's face pale in front of many. Where do we learn that? From Tamar; for it is written (Gen. 38:25): Tamar let herself be led out to be burned rather than publicly shame her father-in-law. What is more, she left it to him to confess his guilt himself. As she was led out, she sent [word] to her father-in-law [BM 59a].

Two contemporaries of Jesus pursue, to their ultimate logical conclusion, the negative consequences of our being made in the image of God. Rabbi Nathan taught, "Anyone who hates a neighbor [i.e., does a neighbor an injustice] uproots God from the world" (ARN 30).

Rabbi Ben Azzai tears away the final mask from hate of neighbor when he teaches, "You should not say, 'Because I have been scorned, may my neighbor also be scorned similarly. . . .' If you act in such a way, know that you scorn the One in whose image that person was made" (Gen R 24:7 on Gen. 5:1).

An exegesis of Exodus 20:26 runs:

If it is said even of the stones of the altar, which have no knowledge of good and evil: "You must not deal with them contemptuously," then how much more is it a logical conclusion that you must not deal contemptuously with your neighbor, who was created in the image of the One who spoke and the world came into existence [Mekhilta].

Between the prohibition of "carrying hatred for your brother in your heart" (Lev. 19:17a) and the commandment "to love your neighbor as yourself" (Lev. 19:18), there stands the charge, "Admonish, yes, you must admonish your neighbor, so that you do not sin because of him" (Lev. 19:17b). On the one hand, it was agreed by the rabbis that "All Israel is responsible for one another" (Shebuoth 39b), that no one may look on indifferently as fellow human beings walk into disaster without trying to restrain them; on the other hand, this obligatory rebuke can lead only too easily to a public humiliation of one's neighbor, a serious sin. It was and is correct, therefore, to find a middle way with tact and sensitivity. Jesus, who, in accord with the rabbis, expressed his care for all Israel by deciding that twelve would be the number of his disciples in his circle of followers, was especially concerned with "the sick who need a physician" (Matt. 9:12)—namely, sinners, prostitutes, renegades, and the hated tax collectors, all of whom he hoped to stir to repentance.

How he could achieve this is told by the story of how he unexpectedly invited himself to the home of Zacchaeus the tax collector. "They all began to murmur because Jesus had gone to the home of such a sinner" (Luke 19:7). But the goal of his visit was conversion, and in fact the meal was hardly finished when Zacchaeus broke out quite spontaneously, "See, Lord, I am giving half my property to the poor, and if I have defrauded anyone I am restoring it four times over" (Luke 19:8). None of this was requested of Zaccheaus, no penitential sermon was directed at him, he was not embarrassed within his family circle. Yet he understood the warning in Jesus' broad hint. A "wayward sheep" found the way back to the flock. It is in this sense that Jesus' counsel of comradely correction is to be understood (Matt. 18:15–17).

In the text of the Instruction on the Mount we read further:

If you bring your offering to the altar and there remember that your brother has something against you, then leave your sacrifice there before the altar and go, be reconciled first with your brother, and then come and present your offering [Matt. 5:23–24].

This sentence is a complement to the preceding two verses, figuratively turning the tables. At first the focus was on those who could offend others, to discourage them by a triple proclamation of punishment; now sufficient empathy is demanded of them to imagine themselves in their injured brother's shoes. And one step more! At the precise moment when they are about to fulfill the holiest act before God, they are to look briefly into their own soul to recall the psalmist's question of conscience, "Who may ascend the Lord's mountain, and who may stand in his holy place?" David's answer: "Whoever has innocent hands and is of pure heart" (Ps. 24:4). In other words, whoever has not sinned against one's neighbor.

Should, however, this interior accounting on the way to the altar lead to the conclusion that one of your fellow humans has something against you—whether with or without cause is deliberately left open—then go and *first* settle that half-suppressed quarrel with your brother or sister so that you come before God "with a pure heart."

For this reason the holiest day in the Jewish calendar of feasts is called the Day of Atonement(s), with its concerns for *two* reconciliations: the interhuman and the divine, the first taking precedence over the second, in the sense of Matthew 5:23f:

> The Day of Atonement expiates transgressions between humans and God (with proper remorse); it does not expiate transgressions between human and human, unless the guilty one has first appeased the neighbor [Yoma VIII, 9].

To put it another way, the horizontal reestablishment of peace, which is much more difficult than communal prayer of repentance, is an absolute prerequisite for the right to beseech God for vertical reconciliation.

How much more difficult it is to face an offended person, to swallow one's pride, and to offer an apology than to go into the synagogue and confess one's sins together with the congregation! Yet it is precisely in this personal sacrifice that we must wring from our egos proof of the seriousness of our aspirations to reconciliation.

This priority of the interhuman is also seen in the Our Father. "Forgive us our trespasses as we *have* forgiven those who trespass against us" (Matt. 6:12). The statement is clear in the language of both Judaism and Jesus: only the self-transcendence of asking for forgiveness and the personal courage of extending one's hand (with all the danger of being rebuffed) can bring the forgiveness that comes from above. In view of the difficulty of the first, the "Ten Days of Repentance" preceding the single Day of Atonement are dedicated to this horizontal peacemaking. In Jewish tradition they are very closely connected with that great lapse into sin committed by all Israel in the infancy of its peoplehood: the worship of the golden calf.

"And now leave me; my anger will be aroused against them, so that I destroy them!" Such is God's decision, issued to Moses. And yet the promise is made, "And you I will make into a great people" (Exod. 32:10).

What happens after this marked the Israelite understanding of both the human and the divine. Moses, "the most modest of humans," interpreted God's opening words—"and now leave me"—to mean that the divine decree was not yet final—that, in fact, the Lord of the world welcomes human collaboration.

This collaboration is threefold, as Moses frames it: a candid admission of his people's guilt, an appeal to God's forebearance and mercy, and a crowning statement of selfless love of neighbor, "Forgive them their sins, but if not, then delete me from the book [of life] that you have written!" (Exod 32:32). It was this exemplary self-denial, slighting himself for love of his people in order to argue with God in terms of his life alone, that ultimately obtained divine forgiveness for Israel.

Chapter 6

BREAKING THE MARRIAGE BOND
(Matt. 5:27–32)

ADULTERY

Whereas the first "superthesis" aims at reinforcing the prohibition of murder as the foundation of all peaceful coexistence, the second "superthesis" turns to the key commandment dealing with the human two-in-oneness of man and woman:

You have heard that it was said: You are not to commit adultery (Exod. 20:14). And I say to you: Anyone who looks at a woman with longing has already committed adultery with her in his heart [Matt. 5:27–28].

Actually there is nothing new in this "reinforcement" of the Torah, for the sayings of Solomon, in the spirit of the tenth commandment, already warn, "Let your heart not long for the beauty of your neighbor's wife, nor let her captivate you with her glance" (Prov. 6:24f.). Here desire is denounced as mother of the deed and the eye as gateway to sin.

Another Jesus, who preached in Jerusalem more than two centuries before the Nazarene, dedicated an entire chapter to proper dealings with women, from the maiden to the wife, the "foreign woman," the musician, the "charming woman," and the harlot, of whom he warns, "Give yourself not up to her, lest she destroy your inheritance" (Sir. 9:6).

The Book of Wisdom of Jesus, son of Sirach, warns of the road to adultery: "Do not go wine-drinking with a married woman . . . , lest your heart tend toward her and in your passion you sink into ruin" (Sir. 9:9).

This earlier Jesus seems to go even a step further when he warns against all extramarital attraction: "Veil your eyes before a charming woman; look at no beauty that does not belong to you" (Sir. 9:8).

An ancient explanation of the prohibition of adultery says that the Hebrew verb for "to commit adultery" consists of four letters, in order to warn "lest you commit adultery with the hand, or with the foot, or with the eye, or with the heart" (Midrash Hagadol on Exod. 20:14).

Similarly close to Jesus' teaching is the guiding principle of Resh Lakish: "You should not say that only he who commits adultery with the body is called an adulterer. He who commits adultery with his eyes is also such a one" (Lev R 23).

"The eye of the adulterer waits for the evening," says the Book of Job (24:15). From this the rabbis deduce that he is already denounced as adulterer before the act, for he has already committed the sin with his eyes.

A goodly number of further examples could be cited to corroborate the statement of Adolph Schlatter, no friend of the Jews, that "even the highest demands of the Sermon on the Mount were to all intents and purposes nothing new for Rabbinism."[23] One practical consequence is that in the orthodox sections of Jerusalem, New York, London, and Paris, men and women study, work, and pray apart—and women visitors in miniskirts or shorts are politely but clearly asked to put their charms on display elsewhere.

DIVORCE

If adultery committed in the heart is equated with profanation of the marriage bond, then—logically—divorce must be as good as forbidden; both offend against the benevolent will of God who created humankind as a couple (Gen. 1:27), intended for oneness (Gen. 2:24).

It is further said: He who sends his wife away should give her a letter of divorce (Deut. 24:1). And I say to you: Anyone who sends his wife away, except for infidelity, causes adultery to be committed with her, for whoever marries the dismissed woman commits adultery [Matt. 5:31–32].

This means that by divorcing his wife, who can now remarry, the husband has misled her into adultery, for "what God has joined together no one should separate" (Matt. 19:6), as Jesus later said in good biblical style. But infidelity is excepted, for through it the marriage is already de facto broken and what was divinely united has thus been severed, so that in this case the letter of divorce is only a confirmation of the accomplished fact. Clinging to a shattered marriage, it is here suggested, would be worse than the juridical confirmation that it has already disintegrated.

Even if the reference to adultery as valid grounds for divorce is lacking in the two parallel passages (Mark 10:11 and Luke 16:18), there is no reason to consider the words "except for infidelity" a later addition intended to weaken Jesus' original statement. On the contrary, they emphasize that marriage is the firmest bond humans enter into with one another. It is even stronger than the bond between parents and children, for for its sake "a man will leave his father and mother and cling to his wife and they will be one flesh" (Gen. 2:24).

Because God created humanity "as man and woman" (Gen. 1:27), rabbinic thought considers a bachelor only half a person, who needs his other marriage-half for full humanization (Yeb 63a). Together they are not two, but one *individuum*, which originally designated something "indivisible" in the sense of "self-sustaining," a two-part unity willed by God. As the basic unit of all communal living on earth, marriage is incorporated in the plan of creation as an indissoluble bond of which God is the covenant-mediator. In the first chapter of the Bible, after each of the first six days of creation, we read, "And God saw that it was good." Only after the creation of the human couple as bearers of God's image does it say, "God saw everything that he had made, and indeed it was *very good*" (Gen. 1:31).

"I will betroth myself with you for all eternity," God says to his people in the words of marital vows, "I will betroth myself to you in righteousness and justice, in grace and mercy" (Hos. 2:21). The divine covenant and the marriage covenant are sealed with the same solemn word, *berith*.

Because every marriage ceremony is understood to be holy—in Hebrew it is called *kiddushin*, "consecration"—God appears with Adam and Eve in rabbinic tradition as the first "best man" (Gen R 8:8), as witness at every wedding (Mal. 2:14), and as tireless matchmaker, for every happy marriage is a divine miracle, greater than the parting of the Red Sea (Pesikta 11b).

Still not every marriage is happy, as Jesus with his insight into human nature was aware, and because from the very beginning God endowed humans with the freedom to choose between good and evil (Gen. 4:7), humans can refuse to obey God (Gen. 2:16f.) as well as break faith with their partners. Adultery therefore is polygamy as well as an obliteration of the sanctified I-you bond by the addition of a third person to a marriage relationship.

"It is not good for a person to be alone" (Gen. 2:18). For the sensitive listener another message can be heard in God's words: three together is still worse! For then one person, or more than one, are degraded to the level of object; the uniqueness of a covenant of two equal partners concluded before God degenerates into a triangle of lifeless, loveless I-it relationships—a dehumanization of the holiest of all interhuman ties.

"How could I commit such a great misdeed and sin against God?" (Gen. 39:9), says Joseph "the righteous," as the Talmud admiringly calls him, in defending himself against the seduction of Potiphar's wife. His question has a double meaning; the adultery asked of Joseph is not only an assault on marriage as such but also a sin against the heavenly creator of marriage.

Whoever does such a thing, says Jesus, has broken and severed monogamy, as the Creator made marriage by eternal law. That the idea of two persons "consecrated to each other" also inheres in the German word *Ehe*, or marriage, was demonstrated by Martin Buber. In one of his letters he writes:

When a friend gets married, I like to turn to what Jacob Grimm had to say about marriage—that in the Gothic word *aiva* from which the German word *Ehe* comes, eternity and law dwelled alongside one another before they separated into *ewe* (eternity) and *e* (law). To me more seems to be said here than that marriage is a matter of eternal order. Our attention is drawn to the fact that the individual who forms a matrimonial alliance with another person and lives accordingly may experience in a special way, a way open only to such a one, the eternal character of human existence.

Jesus' statement, limiting divorce to the exceptional case of infidelity but not forbidding it, is often used by Christian exegetes as (the sole) evidence to portray Jesus as a Torah-tamperer who "placed himself above the authority of Moses." But even if one concedes that the parallel versions in Mark 10:11 and Luke 16:18, both of which insist on the absolute indissolubility of marriage, are originally from Jesus, there is no reason to interpret his teaching as in conflict with the Torah.

The opposite is much more credible, for in Jesus' time it was customary that, when Torah passages differed from contemporaneous circumstances, so that a literal exegesis and application threatened to run counter to the original intention, the rabbis would use liberal interpretive norms in explaining them.

That the rabbis considered God's will a progressive loving dynamic, not a static written document, is clear from the following Talmudic excerpt, which is not lacking in humor and a sense of irony. This didactic parable reflects on what Moses might have experienced had he been transported to Rabbi Akiba's classroom a thousand years after his time:

> When Moses climbed up [to receive the Torah] he saw the Lord of the world sitting there and winding wreaths [or crowns or "little strokes"] around the letters of the Torah.
>
> Then Moses spoke: "Lord of the world, who is stopping your hand?" [That is, who stops you from giving the Torah without these little crowns, which are intended to avoid eventual errors in reading or transcribing?].
>
> The Eternal One responded: "A man will arise after many generations by the name of Akiba ben Joseph; he will one day deliver whole heaps of teachings on every one of these little strokes." Then Moses said to him: "Let me see him!" He answered: "Turn around." And Moses sat down silently in

the eighth (and last) row of the school and listened to the words of the famous biblical exegete.

But despite the greatest attention, he understood almost nothing of what was taught there—and he was quite dismayed. Then Rabbi Akiba came to a moot point, and one of the pupils asked the teacher whence he could know all this. Akiba answered with the traditional formula of the Talmudic fathers: "It is a halakah (rule of life) entrusted to Moses on Sinai." When Moses heard this conclusion, he sighed with relief and leaned back, reassured [Menahoth 29b].

Between the lines of this edifying story five lessons are to be found:

1) The sages in Israel never took themselves too seriously, for here it is admitted that even "Moses, our teacher," as he is respectfully called in the tradition, would never have imagined the ingenious scriptural exegesis of the later rabbis. Even more, he would not have been able to keep up with the class, as is here admitted somewhat archly.

2) Moses is here completely demythologized, for he fails to understand Rabbi Akiba, even after Akiba's concluding statement referring to Sinai. Moses, "the loyal servant of God," is reassured only because he tacitly accepts that God, who gave him the Torah, perhaps had written much more into it than he, Moses, was able to understand in his time.

3) Accordingly, there is here also a commission to interpret further—if necessary even in contradiction to Moses himself, as long as "theological logic" justifies it.

4) At the same time, however, a warning is issued against any overinterpretation that totally abandons the literal meaning and loses its way in exaggerated allegories. That is the meaning of the "little strokes," which are intended to be preventive measures against the twisting of letters and texts.

5) Not least, there is a reminder here of the complexity of the Bible text, which calls for continual reexamination and plumbing of the scriptures to explore their unfathomable depths. In other words, it is not the literal sense that is the final court of appeal for the teacher of Judaism, but rather the original intention, which is accessible only to those digging deeply. Not hairsplitting but search-

ing for meaning is the preeminent precept of the great Jewish interpreters of the Bible, of whom the rabbi from Nazareth was one.

And so there was a teaching in the school of Hillel that a pagan baptized (in the Jewish *mikveh)* but not circumcised was to be counted as a full proselyte (Yeb 46a Bar), although Genesis 17:12, Exodus 12:48, and Leviticus 12:3 make circumcision the immutable "sign of the covenant."

The death penalty for ill-mannered sons (Deut. 21:18-21) was likewise so restrictively narrowed that the Talmud states with satisfaction, "There never has been an intractable son, nor will there be such a one" (Tos Sanh 11:6; Sanh 71a).

The same holds for the command to annihilate an idolatrous city (Deut. 13:13-17), of which the Talmud says, "A case of an apostate city has never occurred and will never occur" (Sanh 71a). Slavery and polygyny, which are common in the Bible, were also abolished by the rabbis.

That even individual rabbis could bring about essential changes in the application of Torah statements we learn from Hillel, who circumvented the year of remission of debts in favor of the poor, widows, and orphans (Shebiith X, 3f.), and abolished the breaking of the calf's neck as expiation for a murder by an unknown hand (Deut 21:1-9) on the basis of Eliezer ben Dinai's initiative (Sotah IX, 8f).

Finally, there is Rabbi Johanan ben Zakkai to be thanked for "putting an end to" the procedure of "the water of bitterness" in the case of women suspected of adultery (Num. 5:11-31). A passage from the prophets is cited as the basis: "I will not punish your daughters when they prostitute themselves and your daughters-in-law when they commit adultery, for the men themselves go off with whores" (Hos. 4:14). The motivation behind the repeal is quite clear: if the men themselves commit adultery, the original reason for forcing the woman into the ceremony of drinking the bitter waters—to preserve or reestablish the man's honor—collapses.

Thus we have here, just as in Jesus' statement on divorce, a rabbinic decision that "put an end to" or narrowed a Torah statement in order to protect women, to allow greater justice to be done them, and to dismantle privilege contrary to the spirit of the Bible.

The rationale behind all the reinterpretation and alteration is quite plain: if the spirit and text of the Torah seem to contradict one another, the rabbis without hesitation always give precedence to the former. "For I desire love and not sacrifice, knowledge of God and not burnt offerings" (Hos. 6:6) is a text to which both Jesus (Matt. 9:13; 12:7) and his teaching colleagues often refer in their new but Torah-true interpretations.

Of the Torah verse, "Uphold my statutes and my ordinances; whoever fulfills them will thereby live" (Lev. 18:5), Rabbi Jehudah explains, "Let him live by them; let him not die by them" (b Yoma 85b; AZ 27b). The fundamental principle resulting from this is, "Mortal danger displaces the Sabbath" (b Sabbath 123a), which holds not only for the Sabbath commandment but for all Torah prohibitions with the exception of the three cardinal offenses: idolatry, incest, and murder (Maimonides, *Hilchot Jessode Ha-Torah*, V, 1–2:7). Thus the sanctity of human life overrides almost all the rules of the Torah, whose life-promoting spirit is given priority over any individual regulation.

All believers in the letter are clearly reprimanded in the Talmud by Raba: "How stupid are those who stand up before a Torah scroll but remain seated before a great teacher of Torah. Although the Torah speaks of forty strokes [as corporal punishment; Deut. 25:2f.], our sages came and reduced it to thirty-nine" (Makkoth 22b).

Jesus in his approach to divorce is thus in the best rabbinic company, for the luminaries of Israel were without exception of the same opinion as Paul, who thought it necessary to proclaim in Corinth, though not in Jerusalem, that "the letter kills, but the spirit enlivens" (2 Cor. 3:6).

In brief, from the time of Abraham on, Judaism is a constantly developing religion. Reinterpretation, spiritual digestion of new experiences, and the constant pursuit of truth: these are its characteristic features, upholding only the essence of faith as the eternal center, subordinating all else to the dynamic of life. Thus the Judaism of Moses is not identical with that of the period of the Judges, and this for its part is considerably different from King David's way of faith. These are followed by the changes of the exile, of those returning from Babylon, of the Maccabees, the Pharisees, and the rabbis who without exception explored further, interpreted anew, and were always able to adapt their Judaism to the spirit of their time.

Finally it must be emphasized that neither divorce nor the drinking of the bitter water, and certainly not the stoning of unruly sons, presents a commandment meant to be obeyed; rather they comprise a legal system intended more to deter than to be implemented. They are more a concession to human weakness than an instruction from on high; they exist "because of the hardness of your hearts," as Jesus rightly says of the writ of divorce (Matt. 19:8).

For a correct understanding of Jesus' dispute with the divorce law of his time, we must return spiritually to the historical circumstances of the teacher on the Mount and his biblical exegesis.

Divorce in Jesus' Bible was regulated according to the ethos of the early days of Israel. The husband was ceded the right, if somewhat reluctantly, to divorce the wife, though only after delivering a valid writ of divorce (Deut. 24:1ff.). The grounds for divorce are ambiguous: "If he discovers something *improper* in her." A legitimate quarrel over this flared up among the Torah exegetes, whose attitudes in so many arguments strike us as almost modern. A generation before Jesus, Rabbi Shammai taught that a divorce is to be assented to only if a proved act of adultery is involved. The "improper" (or disgraceful), as the fifth book of Moses puts it, is for him simply and solely infidelity, which he considers the only valid grounds for divorce. His school cites the prophet Malachi, who declares divorce a sin against God. In this spirit the Talmud says:

> Rabbi Eliezer said: Even the altar sheds tears on the one who divorces his first wife, for it says: And this you will do for the second: cover the Lord's altar with tears, with weeping and moaning, because he no longer looks upon your offering and accepts nothing from your hand with pleasure (Mal. 2:13). And you ask why? Because the Lord has been a witness between you and the wife of your youth, toward whom you have acted faithlessly. And she is yet your partner and the wife of your covenant (Mal. 2:14) [Sanh 22a].

The school of Hillel, on the other hand, begins its exegesis with an Aramaic translation of the Book of Deuteronomy in which "the improper" is interpreted as "violation of a word." This violation, understood as a refusal to obey, was soon broadened to include a breach of one of the marriage stipulations, a transgression of a Torah commandment by the woman, or any behavior that was likely to bring her husband into bad repute.

After the late period of kings, however, divorce gradually was made more difficult in favor of the wife and an eventual salvaging of the endangered marriage. To protect the husband from acting recklessly, a complicated procedure regarding the wording, production, and delivery of the writ of divorce was introduced. At her marriage every wife was presented a marriage contract in which a considerable compensation was awarded her in case of divorce, and she was given the right, in the case of illness, any "physical defect" of her husband, or "repulsiveness" as the result of his employment, to demand the dissolution of the marriage.

So, for example, in regard to the compensation defined at the wedding, we read:

> In the beginning they prescribed 200 sus for a virgin and a mina [100 sus] for a widow; then the men grew old and could not marry women. Then the rabbis decreed that they should leave this [the sum of money named in the marriage contract] behind in the home of their fathers. But if he was angry with her he could still say to her: Go to your marriage gift [which was deposited in her parents' house]. Then the rabbis decreed that they should leave this behind in their father-in-law's house. The rich turned it into little silver or gold baskets, the poor turned it into a vessel for urine. But if he was angry with her he could still say to her: Take your wedding gift and go! Until Simeon, Shetah's son, came and decreed that he must prescribe for her: All my possessions are liable for her compensation [Ket 82b].

Through Rabbi Simeon's decree a hundred years before the Christian era, on the one hand, divorce was made more difficult and, on the other, the security of the marriage contract was guaranteed. In both ways, however, the legal position of the wife was strengthened.

As opposition to divorce increased, the number of paeans glorifying the good husband grew. "Of the one who loves his wife as himself and honors her more than himself and guides his sons and daughters on the right path. . . , scripture says (Job 4:24): 'And you will know peace in your dwelling' " (Yeb 62b).

Equally emphasized by the rabbis was the suffering power of the much-tested husband:

> Three persons do not see purgatory [because they already have hell on earth]: the one who has to make do in oppressive poverty, the one who suffers from abdominal pains . . . and the one who has a nasty wife . . . ; whoever accepts those sufferings out of love earns the atoning force that protects from hell [Erubin 41b Bar].

At the same time rabbinic pronouncements against reckless divorce also increase:

> To him who would repudiate his wife lightly it is said: Prepare nothing evil against your neighbor, because he lives next to you with confidence (Prov. 3:29); . . . likewise: I hate divorce, says the Lord (Mal. 2:16); . . . therefore do not break marital fidelity! [Gettin 90a–b].

"Rab Shaman ben Abba said: Come and see how severe a divorce is: It was permitted King David to live together with Abishag (1 Kings 1:1ff.); but it was not permitted him to repudiate one of his eighteen wives" (Sanh 22a).

Finally it was also pointed out that one who forgoes divorce can be numbered among the imitators of God:

> If a man has married a woman and found something improper in her . . . , he can issue her a writ of divorce (Deut. 24:1, 3, 4) . . . but the Holy One, praised be he, did not act so, for although Israel deserted him and paid homage to others, he said to them: Do penance and turn back to me, and I will accept you again (Jer. 3:1) [Pesihta Rabbati 184a; cf. Yoma 86b].

From early times rabbinic opponents of divorce referred to the biblical law for protection of violated women:

> If someone meets a virgin who is not betrothed and he seizes her and lies with her . . . then he shall pay her father fifty silver pieces and shall take her to wife. . . . He may not dismiss her as long as he lives [Deut. 22:28f.; cf. Exod. 22:15].

If, then, the husband may not dismiss a violated woman whom he had to marry against his will, how much the less can he repudiate the wife of his free choice to whom he has vowed eternal loyalty at the wedding, "as the Lord was witness between you and the wife of your youth" (Mal. 2:14). This was the inference made by a few of the Shammaites.

And yet it is precisely the great number of voices raised against divorce at that time, the variety of their arguments, and the often passionate presentation of their evidence that give us the impression that there was no lack of Hillelites who, in easing the divorce process, were sometimes prepared to make facile, even frivolous, judgments (Ket VII, 6).

It is against the background of this constructive, academic controversy, out of which a synthesis in the form of obligatory divorce law would crystalize only one hundred fifty years later, that we must read Jesus' dialogue with some Pharisees reported for us by Matthew:

> Pharisees came to him who wished to test him and asked him, "May one dismiss [divorce] his wife for any reason?" But he answered them, "Have you not read (Gen. 1:27) that the Creator made humankind from the beginning as male and female, and said (Gen. 2:24), Therefore a man will leave his father and his mother and cling to his wife and the two will be one flesh? What, then, God has joined together, no one should separate." "Why, then, did Moses command (Deut. 24:1) that the woman be given a writ of divorce and then be dismissed?" He answered them, "Moses permitted you [only] because of the hardness of your hearts to divorce your

wives. But in the beginning it was not so. I say to you: Whoever divorces his wife—except for infidelity—and marries another commits adultery" [Matt. 19:3-9].

Of the dozen or so stylistic details by which the hand of the Greek redactor can be recognized here, only two will be mentioned. No Jew would ever have said of a Torah regulation that it was commanded by Moses (Matt. 19:8), for it is an essential part of the Jewish faith that the Torah is God-given, not a legislative work of Moses. Nor was it "commanded" that writs of divorce be presented; the practice was merely "permitted," as Jesus rightly corrects them.

Offhand it seems as if Jesus is attempting to evade the Pharisees' question, which is also asked in the Mishna (Gettin IX, 10). Yet this is not the case. To proclaim the will of God he returns to the creation story to compare it with the writ of divorce granted in the fifth book of Moses. The result is apparent: God has yielded to human weakness and permitted his servant Moses to concede the writ of divorce as an escape hatch "because of the hardness of your heart"—just as Maimonides more than a thousand years later explained the introduction of animal sacrifice (*Moreh Nebuchim*, 3:26-49).

Yet even in Jesus' Bible itself this idea of divine concession to human inadequacy is in no way unique. So, for example, the consumption of meat after the deluge is a concession to human custom (Gen. 9:2-4). The establishment of the kingdom in Israel occurred against the will of God, who yielded to the urgent desire of the Israelites (1 Sam. 8:7-9). The temple in Jerusalem was also originally a desire of Solomon, to whom God in the end gave way (1 Kings 8:2-7, 9:3).

The rabbinic statement on Psalm 94:15 holds true for all these divine "compromises"; God says: "Human beings are hardhearted for a time; therefore I give them time, for if they do penance, then I will accept them again" (Midrash Tehillim on Ps. 94:4).

Just this repentance, in the original Hebrew sense of "return" to God and God's plan of salvation, is the object of Jesus' preaching (Mark 1:15 and parallels), which focuses on Moses' frequent exhortation, "Put aside your hardness of heart and henceforth be not obstinate" (Deut. 10:16). The rabbinic exegesis implies: Take God's commandments to heart, and fulfill them according to God's will. In fact, the goal of the divine pedagogy can be said to be "to plant [God's] law in their heart and to write it in their mind" (Jer. 31:33), so that the fulfilling of God's *original* will no longer requires outer compulsion but instead becomes an inner impulse.

Jesus, like many other rabbis, finds this original will of God at the beginning of his Bible, before the original fall. Jesus illustrates this will of the Creator with three citations from the Book of Genesis in which the duality of all creatureliness is highlighted: heaven and earth, sun and moon, day and night, light and darkness, water and dry land, and, last, man and woman, intended to complement one another so that in becoming one in married love they experience their perfection. "What God has joined together, no one *ought* to separate," Jesus said in good rabbinic style; but the human being *can* separate it, as the abuse of creation, defection from God, and, not least, divorce has proved since the fall.

This power of sin has also transformed the harmony of becoming-one-flesh into a battle of the sexes, a struggle of victory and defeat, of lordship and subjection, making the order of creation deteriorate into an order of destruction.

"But in the beginning it was not so." In Jesus' words can be heard not only sadness over all the evil since the deluge but also an insatiable yearning for the reign of God that will reestablish the conditions of primal time: unbetrayed love, freedom from sin, the presence of God, and an end to all wickedness on earth. What once was, shall be once again: the innocence of paradise is elevated into a dream of the "last days," when the second Adam will wipe out the guilt of the first through superabundant repentance and conversion. This merging of tenses suggests the spirit of the Hebrew language, which has no tenses in the sense of distinctions of time, unlike Greek, Latin, German, and English. "It was" and "it shall be" so strongly resemble one another in the idiom of the Bible that often only the context distinguishes what has already been from what is yet to be, in an eternal present that becomes the bridge of all times. The hastening of the coming of this primal/final time demands that humans, as God's collaborators, foster a unificative attitude that rejects all division—in the form of separation—as unworthy of humans, so that God's joining together may be actualized in its unbounded fullness.

Jesus was indeed not only a herald of the final eon but also an earth-bound realist who wanted to build bridges between tomorrow's vision and today's present. The result is Jesus' radical narrowing of divorce to the case of marital infidelity—in the spirit of the restrictive interpretation of the school of Shammai.

Chapter 7

OATHS
(Matt. 5:33-37)

You have further heard that it was said to our ancestors, "You shall swear no false oath, but you shall fulfill your oath to the Lord!" (Exod. 20:7; Num. 30:3; Deut. 23:22). And I say to you: Do not swear at all, neither by heaven, for it is God's throne, nor by the earth, for it is his footstool, nor by Jerusalem, for it is the city of the great king. And you shall not swear by your head, for you cannot make a single hair white or dark. Let your yes be a yes, your no a no; what goes beyond this comes from the evil one [Matt. 5:33-37]

Jewish tradition distinguishes between an oath of witness to substantiate or reject a testimony before a court; a purification oath of debtors disclaiming a part of the demand directed against them; oaths and vows with which one imposes an obligation upon oneself before God (Num. 30:3; Deut. 23:22ff.); and solemn affirmations that one hopes to make more credible by mention of God, as for example the statement of the Shunammite woman, "As the Lord lives and by the life of my soul, I will not leave you" (2 Kings 4:30). For each of these, however, the words of the Bible hold: "If you had refrained from making the vow, no guilt would come upon you" (Deut. 23:23). Qoheleth, the wise preacher, confirms this: "It is better that you not make a vow than that you make a vow and not fulfill it" (Eccles. 5:4).

The early exegetes reinforced this abstinence from oaths by erecting a moral "hedge around the Torah":

Moses said to Israel: Do not believe that I have permitted you
to swear even in truth by his name. If you possess all these
qualities [fear and love of God, honesty, knowledge of the
Torah, etc.], you may make an oath. If you do not, then you
have no right to do so [Tanhuma Wayikra 7].

The rabbis went a step further and warned emphatically against
procrastination in fulfilling vows:

They who vow and delay in their vows fall ultimately into
idolatry, unchastity, bloodshed, and slander. From whom do
we learn all this? From our father Jacob. Because he vowed
(Gen. 28:20–22) and delayed in his vows he fell into all of
these: idolatry (Gen. 35:2), unchastity (Gen. 34:1), bloodshed (Gen. 34:25), and slander (Gen. 31:1) [Lev R 37].

Because the rabbis had very early disapproved of any mention of
God in an oath as a misuse of the holy name, in accordance with
Exodus 20:7, and equated it with an empty or false oath (Lev.
19:21), many Jews proceeded to use such divine circumlocutions as
"the Gracious," "the Merciful," or "the Forbearing" in their
vows. When this too was forbidden, they dropped the word "oath"
from affirmation oaths, and said simply "by heaven," "by the
temple," "by the convenant," or "by the sanctuary" (i.e., Jerusalem).

Jesus disapproved even of resorting to such substitute formulas,
making it clear that none of these weaker phrases can escape God's
omnipresence. Ultimately the heavens are indeed God's throne (Ps.
11:4), the entire earth God's footstool (Isa. 66:1), and Jerusalem
God's city (Ps. 48:3). No matter by what you vow, Jesus warns the
thoughtless, you are inevitably dealing with God.

Even his own head does not belong to the one who swears, "for
from you, Lord, everything comes, and from your hand we have
returned it to you," as King David says in his prayer of thanksgiv-
ing (1 Chron. 29:14)—a biblical truism that the rabbis confirm:
"Give to God from his own things, for you and all that is yours
belong to him" (Aboth III, 8).

Thought through, taking God this seriously can lead to only one conclusion: by renouncing oaths we contribute to the true honor of the Creator and creation. For, looked at in depth, all swearing leads to an inflationary devaluation of all speech, which it unconsciously divides into two categories: that which is confirmed by calling upon God and that which is asserted without such affirmation. But if only statements of the first type are unconditionally true, then all others are seen as only relatively true or half-true or even as merely plausible. Not only is conscience unnecessarily strained, but the mutual trust of listener and speaker also is weakened, and the gate is opened to doubt, hypocrisy, and lies.

Just as abusive words like "fool" and "numbskull" can be slanderous and destructive of love of neighbor (Matt. 5:21–22), so the division of all speech into "two kinds of truth" endangers that basic trust that is the climatic prerequisite for all human coexistence.

The double-edged tongue can be the cause of love and hate, of good and evil, as James describes quite in the spirit of his brother:

> The tongue is only a small member and yet boasts of great things. And how small a fire can set a great forest aflame. . . . With the tongue we praise the Lord and Father, and with it we curse human beings who are created in God's image. From one and the same mouth come forth blessing and curse [James 3:5ff.].

To guarantee absolute confidence and credibility as the foundation of a new, honest form of community, then, requires control of the tongue, avoidance of ambiguity, the blocking off of all escape routes for dissenters and evaders, the binding character of all speech, and, not least, in everything one says to one's neighbor, consciousness of standing before and under the God who is entitled to the entire, undiminished truth.

Similarities in the formulation of this conclusion by various teachers and groups in Judaism are striking. The Letter of James reads like an echo of the Instruction on the Mount: "Above everything, brothers, do not swear, neither by heaven nor by earth nor any other oath, but let your yes be a yes and your no be a no, lest you fall under judgment" (James 5:12).

The Essenes, to whom Jesus' teachings show some relationship, lived by the same standard: "They refuse to swear, for they consider it worse than perjury; for they say that anyone who offends against good faith is already judged, even without God as witness."[24]

A great number of rabbinic statements sound strikingly like abridged versions of Jesus' words. For example, Rabbi Yose ben Yehudah uses a play on words in reference to Leviticus 19:35: "The Torah teaches you that your yes must be honest and your no must be honest" (BM 49a). Abaye, condemning yes-and-no sayers, adds: "One should not say one thing with the mouth and another with the heart" (ibid.).

Rabbi Hunna pleads for an unconditional, undisguised statement of truth: "The yes of the just is a yes, and the no of the just is a clear no" (Midrash Ruth 3:18). In a rabbinical explanation of the Ten Commandments we read, "The children of Israel at the giving of the Torah at the foot of Sinai answered to the no [of the prohibitions] with no; and to the yes [of the commandments] with a yes" (Mekhilta Exod. 20:1).

A model of clarity is given by Rabbi Eleazar: "No is an oath and yes is an oath" (Sheb 36a). This aphorism became a guiding principle for orthodox Jews, who still today do not swear even in court but simply affirm their assent with "yes."

Many Christians, however, act differently, as the Catholic theologian Adolf Holl reports in connection with Jesus' prohibition of oaths:

> The radical nature of this quite possibly authentic saying of Jesus is made the more obvious by the fact that so far Christianity has been unable to live up to it. Even today oaths are required on certain occasions, for instance in a court of law, and oaths are not infrequently sworn in front of a crucifix—the very image of him who forbade this practice.[25]

Be that as it may, we can summarize as follows. Just as the intensified prohibition of killing, including slander, is concerned with the holiness of human life and human dignity, and just as the protection of marriage is concerned with the sanctification of the family as the basic unit of human society, so renunciation of swearing is concerned with the upholding of truth as a foundation of the Torah way of life.

Truth in the Jewish Bible is never an abstraction or a cliché but a living, interpersonal event. It is not a fanaticism elevating precision and pedantry to the status of virtues, but a being-true and a living-true that calls for "doing the truth" (John 3:21). It is occasionally honored more by silence or a life-promoting white lie than by a reckless use of it to box a neighbor's ears, injuring someone else in order to drive home one's own correctness. Truth that does not flow from love and increase love is a sin of the tongue and inhuman.

For unlike Greek truth, which rests on an intellectual foundation, Hebrew truth, *'emet*, is anchored above all in a scriptural ethos that lends it an undeniably theological dimension.

That is why the rabbis put forward three biblical passages in which the biblical text was "altered" for the sake of peace:

> Great is peace, because for its sake God altered what occurred with Sarah (Gen. 18:13) in Scripture: "Shall I really have a child, for I have indeed grown old?" This is how God repeats to Abraham Sarah's words, which according to Genesis 18:12 were, "For my lord [Abraham] is indeed old." God altered the wording so that Abraham would not be angry with Sarah—that is, for the sake of marital peace.
>
> Great is peace, because for its sake will the name of God written in holiness be wiped away in water (Num. 5:23), in order to reconcile the woman suspected of adultery with her spouse and so restore marital peace.
>
> Great is peace, because for its sake scripture altered the word of an angel. [This refers to Judg. 13:3, where the angel says to Manoah's wife, "You are barren and have had no child," which, on the other hand, he later omits when speaking to Manoah (Judg. 13:13).]

If in these three cases marital peace was considered important enough to justify a relaxed approach to the truth even in scripture, then how much more important is the great truth of international peace compared to the narrow-minded literal truth of the hairsplitter! (see Num. 6:26 and Perek Ha-Shalom).

"All commandments of the Lord are truth" (Ps. 119:86); this truth "reaches as far as the clouds go" (Ps. 36:6); it is "protection and shield" (Ps. 91:4) for all who seek God, and with it God "will judge the peoples" (Ps. 96:13). This truth without oath and vow, is told wherever "kindness and truth meet one another and righteousness and peace embrace"(Ps. 85:11).

If we wish to serve this truth, then it must be candidly admitted that in forbidding oaths Jesus was adding nothing new. There is here neither antithesis nor "superthesis," but further proof that the rabbi of Nazareth stood firmly with both feet on rabbinic soil.

Chapter 8

THE HIGHER LAW
(Matt. 5:43–45)

The final two "supertheses," which deal with renunciation of resistance and love of one's enemy, belong together in their import as the double crown of Jesus' master plan for the divinely ordained humanization of the earth.

A survey of world history can distinguish three chief epochs in the progress of human coexistence. As the human race begins its career, violence predominates. Self-defense necessitates community just to ensure survival.

It was a long and bloody path from the law of the fist to the law of equality and impartiality—"the same law for all." Yet even this hard-won law, which was made an abstract principle for the elimination of prejudice, can, like all theories, become an injustice that leads to hate, anger, and war. In the end, the law too requires the force of the state to succeed.

And so humanity came to understand that true righteousness needs a transjuridical dimension for law to become true justice. This insight is the source of the Hebrew *sedakah* that makes grace precede justice by conceding to others the prerogative that only love can give. It is the hopeful recognition that it is not enough to move from antagonistic being-opposite-one-another to indifferent being-alongside-one-another, for humans are also capable of fruitful being-with-one-another, which can climax in a loving being-for-one-another.

Rabbi S.R. Hirsch, the founder of neo-orthodoxy in nineteenth-century Frankfurt, seized upon the same basic ideas when, in his exegesis of Isaiah 53:8, he advocated the interpretation that the Jewish people is destined to exercise an influence on the whole world through its powerlessness and passivity. Property and power, then, would no longer be the normative factors of states and society, for power-politics would be replaced by a theo-politics guided only by ethical principles as they are expressed in the biblical ideal of the theocracy of love.[26] It is to this nonviolent love, which can mature into a mighty power in the heart, putting service and fellowship in the place formerly held by domination, that the Instruction of the Mount is dedicated.

Its three radical demands for renunciation of force climax in the commandment of the so-called love of enemy, which is probably the most frequently cited yet least often practiced saying of Jesus in the entire New Testament.

Because this is the apex of Jesus' ethics—and may also very properly be called the touchstone of the "better righteousness"—our reflection should begin here.

You have heard that it was said, Love your neighbor and hate your enemy. And I say to you, Love your enemy and pray for those who persecute you, so that you may be sons of your father in heaven; for he has his sun rise on evil and good and has rain fall on just and unjust [Matt. 5:43–45].

The first sentence of this well-known passage contains a biblical citation (Lev. 19:18) that Jesus elsewhere holds up as "the preeminent" or "the first" commandment (Mark 12:29ff. and parallels) in response to the question of a scribe testing Jesus' faith (Mark 12:28).

Yet despite the dual preamble—"you have heard" and "that it was said"—which in rabbinic usage always serves to introduce a divine statement from the Torah, here love of neighbor is abridged to the point of distortion.

The evangelist here halves the Hebrew commandment, for he drops both the indispensable phrase "as yourself" and the essential termination "I am (God) the Lord" (Lev. 19:18). Jesus certainly did not forget these two phrases, for anyone who says, "Until heaven and earth pass away neither shall one iota of the Torah pass" (Matt. 5:18), deals very circumspectly with his holy scripture as the word of God.

These omissions in the text, however, do not merely dismember a well-known biblical passage acknowledged by some Talmudic fathers to be a *kelal* or "key" to the Torah, but they also rob love of neighbor of its vertical component in which its theological foundation is grounded. For love of neighbor can be expounded convincingly only from the concept of God's unity, as the theo-logic of the rabbis confirms. If love of neighbor is not to degenerate into a purely horizontal making use of others, into a godless association of unbelieving, even if far-sighted, egotists, it needs a supplement: I am (God) the Lord. For only under the common fatherhood of God does love of neighbor have meaning and significance as fellowship.

That God's uniqueness and love are inseparably bound together is taught by Joseph Albo, one of the great philosophers of religion in the late Middle Ages. He deduces this truth from the fact that the Hebrew words for "love" *('ahabah)* and "unique" *(echad)* have the same numerical value of thirteen. Thirteen, moreover, is the number of God's attributes in the divine self-revelation of Exodus 34:6–7, where all God's qualities are contained in the embodiment of free, unearned, generous love.

The arbitrary omission of "God the Lord" from love of neighbor also removes the prelude necessary to Jesus' crowning conclusion, "that you may be sons of your father in heaven!" Here "sons" in Hebrew can signify not only descendants, but also co-workers, successors, adherents, followers, or imitators.

All of this, it is highly probable, was eliminated by the Greek editor so that the unbiblical hatred of enemies could be inserted—though quite out of context here—into one of Jesus' sayings as an anti-Jewish innuendo.

"NEIGHBOR"

Let us look at the original citation, which Jesus probably presented in its complete form: "Love your neighbor as yourself. I am God, the Lord" (Lev. 19:18).

Just about all German and English editions of the Bible since Martin Luther translate it this way, though the first noun is not rendered quite accurately. "Neighbor," that is, does justice neither to the Greek *plesion*, which means what is "nigh" or "standing near," nor to the Hebrew *reya'* underlying it. *Reya'*—"comrade," "companion"—is, as Buber explains, the person with whom I have to do at this moment, who is encountering me right now: the one who is my concern at this instant, no matter whether a blood relative or a total stranger.

Anyone reading the excerpt of the so-called holiness laws (Lev. 19:9–18) from which Jesus is quoting notices immediately that the divine mandate for the sanctification of the world issued here is aimed first of all at a better communal life among humans.

Emerging just as clearly from Leviticus 19 is the fact that all in need of love, though they may be far beyond tribal borders, are the objects of God's predilection. The concern here is for the poor, the foreigner, the day-laborer, the deaf, the blind, and the lowly, who must be protected from prejudice, calumny, discrimination, or defamation, for "I am the Lord, your God," as we are told five times in explanation. What is meant: "I am the Creator of all life; I love the lowly and the poor just as much as I love you whom I lovingly liberated from the misery of Egyptian slavery, so that you might learn from the experience of suffering the lesson of love, and through it become *my people*, a model for the gentiles!"

If all these directions for building up a more human community culminate in the synopsis, "Love others as fellow humans with whom you have to do," then that means that love is not simply a dual relationship but an attitude concerning both God, who has endowed you with the capacity to love, and the society that you should raise to a higher community of life by little steps of love.

Touchstone of this finely-tuned uprightness is the stranger, who, speaking and thinking and believing quite differently, challenges us to broad-mindedness. "If you offer peace only to your brothers, what are you doing that is special? Do not the pagans also do that?" (Matt. 5:47), as Jesus and the rabbis unanimously stress (see Gittin 62a; Ber 17a; j Ber 8:12c). Yet we are told quite unmistakably: "For the Lord is your God . . . , the great Power and fearsome God, who does not look upon the person . . . and loves the stranger" (Deut. 19:17f.). Therefore "you should love the stranger as yourself" (Lev. 19:34).

Strangers are to be held dear, for they need love just as you do, who need love to live, as your heart tells you every day. That they are like you is confirmed in the Bible by the fact that you suffer as they do. "You know the heart of the stranger, for you too were strangers in Egypt" (Exod. 23:9).

Laid out clearly, this means: You have yourselves experienced enough lovelessness to know what the heart yearns for. As enslaved laborers you have experienced in your own bodies how essential it is to lovingly meet another person halfway, for only strangers tested by suffering have learned how dreadfully hatred can brutalize, whereas love heals and helps both the giver and the receiver toward deepened humanity. The purpose and goal of the chapter-long appeal to kindness (Lev. 19) is that the stranger in biblical Israel not fall into Israel's situation in Egypt, for there are "Egypts" everywhere. The pagan land of Canaan, through the practice of the law of love, *sedakah*, should become the Promised Land that shall eventually embrace the entire world.

Thus the laws of holiness say expressly, "If a stranger dwells among you, you should not oppress him. Let him be to you like a compatriot, the stranger who tarries in your midst" (Lev. 19:33f.). It is not enough to admit that the *reya'* also includes the stranger, for it was precisely the stranger for whose sake the law of love originated. Only when the suspect stranger was able to advance to the level of a fellow human being did the love of strangers become a yardstick of all-encompassing human love in biblical Israel.

Reya' originally meant a hunting companion, and as such can also be an Egyptian (Exod. 11:2), the former despot. Thus he is in no way only "the neighbor" (or "the nearest [one]," *der Neheste*, as Martin Luther and other Germans translated it, using the superlative form of a spiritual, confessional, or ethnic "near," *Nähe*). The "nearest" can also be the most distant where personal characteristics are concerned, but that person nevertheless now stands facing you as a fellow human being.

On the other hand, the "neighbors" closest to you by blood or physical presence can be your archenemies, so that it is precisely their all too palpable nearness that makes them unbearable.

"Who is my *reya'*?" The rabbis, in good Jewish form, respond to this question, which Luke puts into the mouth of a scribe (Luke 10:29), with a counterquestion: Why did God create only one Adam? And they answer: for the sake of worldwide peace, for now no child of Adam can say to someone else: The blood flowing in my veins is redder (or bluer) than yours. Lest pride or racial vanity arise, the Creator has given us one common genetic ancestor. And let no one assert that there are many creative powers in heaven, for this basic unity of humankind proves both the oneness of our Creator and the equality of all Adam's descendants, who without exception come naked into the world, to return to earth equal in the same nakedness.

From the divinely ordained equality found in all human beginnings and endings there flows not only a universal democracy of equal rights, and the pluralistic freedom of belief honored in Jewish society, but also an equal claim to salvation by all of God's offspring. No image of God is salvation-less or love-less or unloved! That is the good news of the Hebrew Bible, drawn irrefutably from the all-oneness of God.

One step more! Nothing else bears so eloquent a witness to God's greatness as the creation of human beings in such inexhaustible variety that even twins are different from one another— and yet human nature is a species, not a genus; there is only one large family of Adam's descendants who all, in their individual uniqueness, have the same rights, are rooted in the same soil, strive for the same heaven, share one and the same human fate, and are equally dear to their Creator.

And who dares hate someone whom God loves? In the words of Rabbi Nathan, "Anyone who hates a *reya'* uproots God from this world" (ARN 30). There are only a few rabbis who sanction the limitations on love of neighbor recommended by Paul: "Let us do good to everyone, but especially to our comrades in faith" (Gal. 6:10).

Jesus' Bible knows no such special privilege, no such priority. It commands that the *reya'* (Lev. 19:18), even if a stranger (Lev. 19:34), be loved as oneself.

According to Ezekiel (47:21-23), aliens have a claim on the division of land. They may buy Hebrew slaves of both sexes. They are legally equal with the natives. One of the threats in the fifth book of Moses reads: "Cursed be the one who perverts the right of the stranger, the orphan, and the widow" (Deut. 27:19).

The six cities of refuge in cases of unintentional homicide—a Mosaic institution to check blood vengeance—are also open to aliens (Num. 35:16). Interest may neither be taken from them nor given them—so it is written in Leviticus 25:35-37, where the stranger is described as a "brother."

That this brother can even be a pagan and an idolater is not infrequently stressed—as, for example, in the exegesis of Leviticus 19:13:

> You should not oppress your *reya'*! Your *reya'* is your brother; your brother is your *reya'*! From this it is learned that stealing from a pagan is theft. And one may not take "only your brother" in a narrow sense, for every human being is meant here [Seder Eliahu Rabba 49].

Jeremiah, speaking in the name of God, says of King Josiah:

> He practiced justice and righteousness,
> he pled the cause of the wretched and poor.
> Is that not to know me?
> Says the Lord [Jer. 22:16].

Here the prophet emphatically equates support given to the defenseless—whoever they may be—with acknowledging God.

In these and similar statements there is no hint of either chauvinism or xenophobia—to say nothing of hatred of enemies—but instead a firm universal equality of rights, which is of messianic inspiration. In fact we are told, "You should not hate your brother *in your heart*" (Lev. 19:17). Not only actual hostility is forbidden here, but even uncurbed feelings like envy, vindictiveness, jealousy, or malevolence, which corrupt the heart that was given human beings to love with.

This *reya'* is thus someone who is not near at all, in all his or her divinely-ordained otherness, who comes to us when it is important for us to be truly human. For according to God's will, true humanization is two-way street—in sharing and communicating the love that God originates. For seen in depth the human person is not an island but a dialogical creature who needs others to bring humanness to full blossom. Chiseled imperishably into the plan of creation is the truth that every "I" requires a "you" through whom to grow, mature, and come of age. The other person is always the concrete, unpredictable earthling whom we meet—though perhaps in confrontation or even antagonism, which does not absolve us from the obligation of love.

For if you become an opponent to your opponent, then you are surrendering what is best in you merely to make the worst of the other your own. Loyalty to yourself, however, demands that you give precedence to your own standards over uncharitable influences from without. Otherwise you become "estranged," lose your self-determination, and hand yourself over to unlove, completely contradicting the ways of God.

In the words of Rabbi Meir, "God says: Be like me! As I repay evil with good, so may you also repay evil with good" (Ex R 26:2 on 17:8).

How central this love of neighbor, understood as active worship, is to Judaism can be seen by the numerous explanations of the passage from Leviticus 19 cited by Jesus, "Love your neighbor as yourself; I am the Lord." In the Hassidic interpretation, the deeper meaning is that wherever two persons love one another selflessly on earth, God is the third party in their covenant.

"BEING-LIKE"

Martin Buber tells the story about how once, after a lecture on love of neighbor, a woman approached him to ask, "I don't love myself at all, Mr. Buber, so how can I love my neighbor?" Buber and Rosenzweig, who were translating the scriptures into German at that time, took this question seriously and reconsidered their biblical text to work out another translation that would be just as true to the original wording and sense. Ultimately they wrote, "Esteem others as you do yourself."

Buber explained that your fellow human, no matter how apparently overpowering, brutal, or inconsiderate, is precisely as weak, feeble, and exposed to all the anxieties of life as you yourself are. This being-like-you disarms any fear that you might have before your *reya'*. And just as fear is disarmed, so too hate, which almost always arises from an undercurrent of fear, becomes pointless and meaningless. And as soon as fear and hate disappear, the gates of the heart open themselves to unencumbered, free love of neighbor.

The students of the rabbi of Slozow asked him one day, "It says in the Talmud that our father Abraham fulfilled the entire Torah. How is this possible, for it had not yet been given at that time?"

"All that is necessary," responded the rabbi, "is to love God and God's creatures! If you wish to do something and you perceive that it could diminish your love, then know that it is sin; if you wish to do something and you perceive that your love will increase through it, then know that your will concurs with God's will. Our father Abraham also held this."

Rabbi Joshua Heschel, one of the great philosophers of religion in our century, said: Love your neighbor; your neighbor is like you. What does the Creator wish to teach us by this? God says, I have created both of you as bearers of my image, so that any hatred of neighbor is nothing else than disguised hatred of me. If you bear a grudge against your neighbors, or revile, abominate, or belittle them, then you do all this to the divine spark that burns in their heart and confers nobility on them.

The mystics of the medieval Cabbala said that the neighbor is always a part of you. In every fellow human you yourself lie in embryo. Nonlove of the neighbor therefore avenges itself on your own ego, which cries out to heaven against the masochism of lovelessness. For every hate, seen in depth, is self-hate. And every instance of love is actually self-love. Altruism is nothing but enlightened self-interest that sparks the imagination enough to "get out of one's skin" and inside someone else's, to empathize with and alleviate the needs of others—as if they were part of oneself.

Even Max Horkheimer, "faith-full" Jewish "heretic," corroborated the same basic idea:

> Looked at from the standpoint of positivism . . . hate is not worse than love. . . .Without reference to the divine, good behavior loses its meaning. . . . Along with the last trace of theology, the idea that the neighbor is to be esteemed, to be loved, loses its logical basis.

Chapter 9

HATE YOUR ENEMY?

After the fragmentary quotation of the commandment to love one's neighbor in Matthew 5:43 there follows in seamless continuity the quotation of a commandment to hate one's enemy, a quotation that could not possibly stem from Jesus himself. The strange imperative, "hate your enemy," turns the ethos of the entire Bible into a lie.

The conjecture that this hatred of one's enemy refers to a precept of the Qumran sect (DSM 1:3f.), where there is talk of "hatred of all the sons of darkness" (i.e., all enemies of the Qumran community), seems somewhat farfetched, for the twofold introduction, "you have heard" and "it is said," is used in the Sermon on the Mount as well as in rabbinical writings to introduce *biblical* traditions.

In Jesus' time the Qumran sect was too young, too distant, and too small to be presumed to have been a recognized norm—or antinorm—in Galilee.

This fact has since been generally recognized. The *Jerusalem Bible* is typical of most commentaries in noting of this alleged commandment to hate one's enemy: "The second part of this commandment is not, and could not be found thus formulated in the Law" (footnote on Matt. 5:43).

Even clearer is Ethelbert Stauffer, who, thanks to his notorious dejudaizing of Jesus in the Hilter era, is above all suspicion of "philosemitism": "The synagogue has always justifiably protested against Matthew 5:43. There is no law that prescribes hatred of one's enemy either in the Old Testament or in the Talmud."[27]

85

It is not impossible that Jesus here used the Hebrew verb "to hate" in its secondary, considerably milder meaning, as we know it from two of his sayings.

Speaking of the conditions of discipleship, he told his followers, "If anyone comes to me and does not *hate* his father and his mother and his wife and his children, and even his own life as well, he cannot be my disciple" (Luke 14:26). On the matter of death and what follows, he says in his farewell discourse "Whoever *hates* his life in this world will preserve it unto eternal life" (John 12:25).

Here "to hate" has the biblical meaning of "attach little value to" or "love less than," as for example in God's words, "I have loved Jacob, but Esau I have hated" (Mal. 1:2-3; Rom. 9:13). The same meaning is found in the passage about the husband with two wives, "one whom he loves, and one whom he hates" (Deut. 21:15), which prompts the rhetorical question in the Talmud, "Are there then beloved and hated persons before God?" (Yeb 23a).

The possibility of this gentler intention on Jesus' part cannot, of course, be absolutely rejected; nevertheless both the biblical tradition at work here and the inner coherence of this "superthesis" speak against it. It thus seems most likely that the final redactor of Matthew's Gospel, who seldom overlooked an opportunity to interweave polemical points and anti-Jewish barbs into his subject matter, is the author of this slander. This view is also supported by the fact that not one word of this "hate" is mentioned in the Lukan parallel of the sermon on the plain.

THE JEWISH TRADITION

The very opposite of hatred of enemies is much more visible in Judaism. Hillel the Wise taught his disciples, "Be of the pupils of Aaron, loving peace and working for peace, loving humans and leading them to the Torah" (Aboth I, 12)—clearly referring to both friend and enemy.

Among the sayings of Solomon we read, "If your enemy should fall, do not rejoice, and if he stumbles, let your heart not gloat" (Prov. 24:17). From this adage the rabbis infer:

At Sukkoth, it says three times in scripture, one must rejoice (Deut. 16:14f.; Lev. 23:40). But at Passover, although it concerns the liberation of the people, joy is nowhere mentioned in the scriptures. Why? Because the [enemy] Egyptians perished [Pessikta K 189a].

And so among the accusations that Job devised against himself, the question of conscience was not forgotten: "Have I rejoiced over the ruin of one who hates me, and been elated because misfortune struck him? No, I did not allow my mouth to sin in damning his soul with a curse" (Job 31:29f.).

Here the enemy is named correctly and precisely: the one who hates me, my subjective enemy, who today is my adversary but need not be tomorrow. But even when the enemy does something unkind to me, that person does not cease to be my *reya'*. For it is written, "Do not take vengeance and do not bear grudges" (Lev. 19:18). And even more clearly, "Do not say, I will repay evil. Hope in the Lord, who will help you" (Prov. 20:22).

Solomon repeats it for the hard of hearing: "Do not say, I will do to him as he has done to me; I will repay everyone according to their acts" (Prov. 24:29). And if Proverbs says (25:22), "The Lord will repay you," then the rabbis alter the reading of this verb (*jashlim* instead of *jeshalem*) to make this last passage read: "The Lord will bring him to peace with you" (Midrash Prov. 25:22). And the Bible says of Israel's archenemies, "You should not detest the Edomite; he is your brother. You should not despise the Egyptian, for you have been a stranger in his land" (Deut. 23:8).

Joseph, as viceroy of Egypt, tells his repentant brothers, "You thought to do evil to me, but God thought to make it good"; this "good" is explained immediately: "that is, to preserve a great people" (Gen. 50:20), meaning the Egyptians.

In rabbinic literature the university of human love often expressly touches on the "hater": "Do not say, I love those who love me and I hate those who hate me, but I love everyone" (Test Gad 6).

The rabbis associate this prohibition of retaliation with praise of humble self-restraint, which they equate with divine love:

Of those who are humiliated and do not humiliate, who hear themselves insulted and do not answer, who act out of love and rejoice in correction, of them it is said (Judg. 5:31),

"Those who love God are as the rising of the sun in its glory"
[Yoma 23a; Gettin 36b].

Because repayment always makes the behavior of the other a
model for one's own action, in the end two bearers of the divine
image suffer: you and your brother. The inference is obvious:
"They are tormented and do not torment; they hear themselves
insulted and do not reply; they act out of love and rejoice in
sorrows; these are the ones who love God" (Shabbat 88b). Yet
because the "hater" need not remain a permanent enemy, but could
be only the victim of a spontaneous impulse of the heart, which like
everything else human is fickle, Rabbi Nathan draws a constructive
conclusion from this situation: "Who is the greatest hero in the
land?" He answers his pedagogical question himself: "The one
who wins the love of an enemy" (ARN 23).

That this lies within the realm of the possible is corroborated by
the rabbis who point out that the difference between "enemy"
(oyev) and "lover" *(ohev)* is but a single letter. Should we not
summon up the strength, we are asked, to change a *y* to an *h*!

To sum up, the rabbinic warning—quite in the spirit of Jesus—
says, "Whoever hates the *reya'* is among those who shed blood"
(Derech Eretz Rabba 11).

IN PRACTICE

How such exalted principles are translated into everyday practice
may be illuminated by a single example representative of many. In
the exegesis of Exodus 21:1f. the Talmud laid down that one must
rescue the burglar who breaks into the house at night and in the
process falls into mortal danger through carelessness, even if this
means violating the Sabbath (San.72b). Rabbi Nechonia taught his
pupils to pray, "May it be your will . . . that no hate mount against
us in a human heart, that no one be jealous of us and that we be
jealous of no one else . . . and that all our works be well-pleasing
before you like supplications" (j Ber 4:7d).

So impressive was a similar prayer by Mar bar Rabina that even
today it is recited three times each day in the synagogue liturgy:
"My God, guard my tongue from evil, my lips from untruth. Let
my soul be silent before those who curse me, and may my soul be as

dust against anyone" (Ber 17a) (meaning, "may I ignore all slander, as if it were mere dust—nothing"). That one is not to be content simply with reciting the prayer is attested to by a Jewish war veteran of the first century: "Even the [conquered] enemy should be treated with kindness," wrote Flavius Josephus from his own experience (*Against Apion*, II, 28, 209).

Help, support, and care for the enemy begin in the first book of Moses. There Abraham prays for Abimelech, the king of Gerar, who had taken Abraham's wife Sarah away from him (Gen. 20:17), and interceded with God for the healing of this adversary. And Joseph forgave his brothers who had sold him into slavery, "comforted them and spoke to them as a friend" (Gen. 50:18–21).

Five times Moses prays for the well-being of the pharaoh and those same Egyptians who for centuries had brutally subjugated the people of Israel and intended eventually to exterminate them. "The pharaoh said, I will let you go . . ., but do not go too far, and pray for me! Moses said, . . . I will ask the Lord that tomorrow the flies may depart from the pharaoh and his people . . . . And the Lord did as Moses prayed" (Exod. 8:24–27). The pharaoh, however, repeatedly deceived him and then asked for forgiveness, breaking his word after the termination of each of the first nine plagues—and Moses nevertheless interceded successfully for him and the Egyptian people.

Similarly the sorely tested Job prayed for his false friends who put him off with hypocritical consolation, "and the Lord listened to Job" (Job 42:9).

The same is true of the young David, who spared King Saul who fell into his hands defenseless, although Saul had repeatedly sought to have the shepherd boy murdered. "I have not sinned against you," he said to his archenemy and lord, "but you hunt me down to take away my life" (1 Sam. 24:12).

That David, in displaying such magnanimity, was no exception among the rulers of Israel is shown by the story of the Aramaic king Ben-Hadad, who had waged war against Israel for years until King Ahab was able to overcome him and put his army to flight. Then we read:

> Ben-Hadad fled into the city and hid. . . . Then his servants
> said to him, Look, we have heard that the kings of the house

of Israel are merciful kings. . . . Perhaps he will spare your life. . . . And they went to the king of Israel and said, Your servant Ben-Hadad directs us to say to you, Spare my life! . . . But Ahab said . . . He is my brother! . . .Then Ben-Hadad came out to him. And Ahab had him climb into his chariot . . . , made a treaty with him and let him go [1 Kings 20:30–34].

After Jeremiah had preached in vain to Jerusalem to accept peacefully its subjection to Nebuchadnezzar, the king of Babylonia, the holy city was demolished, the temple laid in ruins, and "the people who remained in the city were yoked together like cattle and driven into captivity" (2 Kings 25:8ff.). In the year 594 B.C.E., the prophet writes to those who had been taken away and whose Babylonian tyrants told them to "sing and be cheerful of heart" (Ps. 137:3): "Seek what is best for the city [Babylon] to which I have let you be exiled." So God speaks, whereupon the prophet demands that the exiles offer prayers for their own suppressors: "And pray for them to the Lord! For if things go well for them, then they will also go well for you" (Jer. 29:7).

The historical events proved him right: the prayer of the exiles was heard and the Babylonian diaspora witnessed one of the most fruitful flowerings in Jewish history.

LOVE YOUR ENEMIES

The Synod of the Evangelical Church in the Rhineland was correct in its statement "On the Renewal of Relationships between Christians and Jews" of November 1, 1980:

In the Jewish and in the Christian tradition God's love embraces the entire creation. As God's image and partner the human being should work according to this divine model. The Jew and the Christian, therefore, may not withdraw love from their fellow humans, even if they should be their enemies—for even the enemy remains God's beloved creature. It is thus not astonishing that in Judaism, before, during, and after the time of Jesus, love of one's enemy was in force. . . . It is therefore incorrect to say that Jesus was the first to free the commandment of love from all restrictions "by mandating love of one's enemy" [p. 27].

And nevertheless it must be stressed that despite the numerous parallels and analogues in Jewish scripture which extend love of neighbor even to the most distant and declare all God's creation worthy of love, the body of Jewish teaching knows no explicit demand of love of one's enemy. To be precise, "love your enemy" is an innovation introduced by Jesus.

Has it become a Christian characteristic in practice, as is suggested in so many sermons and lectures? In his search for exemplifications of love of enemy, theologian Ethelbert Stauffer found only four:

> Jesus himself, who could still pray on the cross: "Father, forgive them, for they know not what they do" (Luke 23:34). The martyr Stephen, who dies with the words, "Lord, hold not this sin against them" (Acts 7:60). James, the brother of Jesus, who prays in the hour of death, "I beg, Lord, God, Father, forgive them, for they know not what they do" (Eusebius, *Ecclesiastical History*, II, 13, 16).[28]

The fourth example is much more recent:

> On October 20, 1958 the Great Chamber of the Supreme Court in Warsaw opened proceedings against [Nazi] District Commander Erich Koch. The accused was brought forth from the Warsaw prison. Koch declared on the first day of trial, "If I am still living, it is thanks solely to a great woman, the prison physician, Dr. Kaminska" [Dr. Kaminska is Jewish].[29]

For the sake of fairness, let me add: all four were Jewish! But they are not the only ones. Typical of the many concentration camp survivors who put down in writing the feelings bottled up in their souls is the short poem of a Jewish woman, Ilse Blumenthal-Weiss:

> I cannot hate.
> They beat me,
> trample me underfoot.

I cannot hate.
I can but atone
for you and me.

I cannot hate.
They strangle me.
They cast stones at me.
I cannot hate.
I can but weep
bitterly.

Jules Isaac, the French Jewish historian and educator, lost his entire family in Auschwitz. Yet in 1947, in his *Jésus et l'Israël*, he succeeded in laying the foundation stone of a Jewish-Christian understanding. It was this book that later induced Pope John XXIII—then yet nuntius in Paris—to place the relationship of the church to Judaism on the agenda of the Second Vatican Council. The final chapter of the book closes with an open question: "The glow of the Auschwitz crematorium is the beacon that lights, that guides all my thoughts. Oh, my Jewish brothers, and you as well, my Christian brothers, do you not think that it mingles with another glow, that of the Cross?"[30]

Leo Baeck was the most recent luminary of the German rabbinate. Three times he was offered the chance to save himself and his family by emigrating during the Hitler years. Three times he rejected the offer, which seemed to him to be fleeing from his assigned task. He wished to remain with his people as teacher "as long as a single Jew remained in Germany," as a history of the camp later put it. He was made a draft horse by the SS, daily transporting carts with buckets from the toilets.

And yet, in the wooden barracks, in the storerooms, and under the open sky, he held evening lectures on Plato and Kant, on Isaiah, Job, and Jesus—a yearlong sermon on the mount out of the depths of the abyss of abandonment, calmly witnessing to the good news of both Testaments. "Our Father in heaven is not dead—even if humans in God's image become inhuman." When the Russians liberated the concentration camp at Theresienstadt, where he was to the end the spiritual center, Rabbi Baeck—by chance or providence—was among the 9,000 out of 140,000 prisoners who had survived the suffering.

"Father, forgive them, for they know not what they do" (Luke 23:34), Rabbi Yeshua once prayed on the Roman cross for his tormentors. In the year 1945 Rabbi Baeck exercised all his personal influence to defend German officers and guards from revenge. As soon as he had recovered spiritually and physically he was among the first to speak in favor of reconciliation between Germans and Jews. His prayer from the first postwar years needs no commentary:

> Let there be peace for those of ill-will, and an end to all vengeance and all talk of penalty and punishment. . . . The atrocities mock all standards; they stand beyond all borders of human comprehension, and the martyrs are many. . . . Therefore, O God, do not weigh their outrages with the scales of righteousness, and hand them over to executioners, demanding a terrible reckoning from them. Deal with them differently. Credit to the murderers and informants, betrayers and all evil persons the courage and the fortitude of the others, their personal modesty, their noble dignity, their silent efforts despite everything, the hope that does not surrender, and the brave smile that dries up tears, and all the sacrifice, all the warm love . . . all the harrowed, tortured hearts that still remained strong and ever-trusting in the face of death and in death, yes, even the hours of profoundest weakness. . . . All that, O my God, should count before you as ransom for the forgiveness of debt, should count for a rebirth of righteousness—all the good should count, not the evil. And in the memory of our enemies we should no longer be their victims, no longer their nightmare and terror, but rather a help that releases them from their frenzy. . . . That is all that is asked of them—and that we, when all this is over, may live again as humans among humans, and that there will be peace again on this poor earth, upon persons of good will, and that peace may also come upon the others.[31]

All that Yitzak Katznelson, a faithful Jew and director of the municipal high school in Lodz, has left us is a poem with the title,

"The Song of the Last Jew." It was written on the way to Maidanek on the back of three envelopes, and although he knew that his destination was the gas chamber, no thoughts of vengeance, not a single word of hate, passed his lips. What he was able to hand on to us as his last statement sounds more like a theology of vicarious expiation that lets the magnificence of his soul shine through:

> Holy on the cross is my people
> atoning for the guilt of the world.
> If ever my people was a chosen people
> because it suffered for others—
> then it is now, now!
> For never yet did a Jew die
> purified like those who seemed so insignificant
> in Warsaw, Vilna, or Lvov.
> For out of every Jew there screams terrified
> a Jeremiah—each is a king
> of disappointment—who weeps for all.

During his first interview with a German journalist, Hans-Joachim Schilde, on November 3, 1978, in Jerusalem, Israeli Prime Minister Menachem Begin was asked, "Can you really still believe in God after Auschwitz?" He answered:

> Yes, I do, because Auschwitz is our sacrifice for God's justice in this world. I believe in God's direction in politics. Had Hitler not killed the Jews, he might have won the war. Were it not for divine providence, Hitler would have been the first to build the atom bomb. . . . Then our world would be one large prison. The Dark Ages would have begun. . . . We Jews made the greatest sacrifice in this battle for the survival of humanity. . . . Perhaps we had to make the sacrifice so that Hitler would lose.

David composed Psalm 109 in the face of a merciless adversary. Verse 4 reads, "Because I love them, they oppose me, but I pray." The rabbinic midrash extends this statement to the painful lot of all Israel: "Instead of loving me they hate me," says Israel to the peoples: "You ought to love us, for we offered 70 annual sacrifices for you in the temple in Jerusalem; yet you do not love us but hate us; however, we pray for you" (Midrash and Yalkut Shimoni on Ps. 109:4).

If practicing love of one's enemy is at the center of Christianity, then I often am not sure who is closer to Jesus—his biological brothers and sisters from Judaism or his baptized followers from the gentile world.

Chapter 10

A LOVE THAT DISARMS

Hating one's enemies, rejoicing in their misfortune, and repaying evil with evil are expressly forbidden in Judaism. Magnanimity and kindness toward an enemy in need are commanded. But love of enemy as a moral principle does still seem to be tailored only for saints, as five thousand years of world history confirm.

When Bismarck said, "No state can be ruled by the Sermon on the Mount," and the West German chancellor commented in 1981 that "it would be an error to understand the Sermon on the Mount as guidelines for governmental action," both were no doubt thinking of this love of one's enemy as a practical program should an emergency, a political conflict, arise.

More surprising is the protest from the other side. Herbert Marcuse, the philosopher of the new left, exclaimed at a student gathering in Berlin in 1968:

> With the Sermon on the Mount one cannot revolt. . . . Hatred of exploitation and suppression is a humane element. . . . Nothing is more abominable than the preaching of love: "Do not hate your opponent"—this in a world in which hate is everywhere institutionalized.

But if one can neither rule nor revolt with this doctrine of love, is it at all possible to live with it or according to it? Leonhard Ragaz is correct in questioning whether it can be fulfilled: "Is that not too much to demand? Can we love those who hate us and do evil to us?. . . Is that not a moral utopia? Is that not an illusion?"[32]

The answer, which can be reached only via a retranslation into Hebrew, is a clear no. Neither sympathy nor maudlin sentimentality, much less self-surrender, are commanded here, but simply and solely "doing"—one of the most common words in Jesus' vocabulary. And, in fact, the commandment of love of neighbor (Lev. 19:18) that Jesus cites here does *not* say "Love your neighbor" in the accusative but in the *dativus ethicus*, a usage that in English can only be paraphrased: "turn to your neighbor lovingly," or "show your neighbor loving acts," or "take care of your neighbor." In a word, "do good, not harm, to your neighbor."

Because Jesus was neither a visionary nor a utopian, but a worldly-wise observer of human nature, he did not demand super-human selflessness or sentiments that would be overdemanding for almost any human heart, but practical demonstrations of love such as visiting the sick, giving alms in secret, supporting the needy, consoling the sorrowful, sharing bread with the hungry, and all the thousand and one effective good deeds that create trust, demolish enmity, and promote love.

Because Jesus loved to preach in parallel, contrasting pairs and in rhetorical antitheses, the intensified "love your enemy" in the original Semitic wording must also have been formulated with the same *dativus ethicus*—by no means a call to a Platonic love of enemy, much less to a hypocritical pretense of love, but to a reconciliation with one's opponent aimed at a long-range rehabilitation.

Jesus also implied this by calling the opponent not "enemy" but "hater," as the Lukan parallel (6:27) suggests. The distinction is considerable for the keen of hearing. For the concept "enemy" indicates in all languages a kind of "full-time occupation," but a limited temporal quality is clear in "hater," a verb functioning as a noun. For the hater is someone who hated you yesterday and still hates you today, but maybe not tomorrow, if you only find the way to that person's heart.

Love of one's enemies, as Jesus understood it, means far more than covering things up with a smile by tolerating enemies or holding them at a distance with politeness; it entails an honest effort, a campaigning and struggling with them, so that they change, give up their hate, and become reconciled. In short—a theo-politics of little loving steps aimed at making the enemy cease to be an enemy. The same is true of praying for one's own persecutor, as a similar episode from the Talmud attests:

> A few dissipated fellows living in the neighborhood of Rabbi Meir pestered him badly. Rabbi Meir prayed that they would die. Then his wife Beruria said to him: "What are you thinking of? Perhaps because it is written, 'May sinners disappear' (Ps. 104:35)? But is it really written 'sinners'? Hardly, for we can also read 'sins' for the same word [as the vowelless wording of Hebrew permits]. Besides, continue the verse to its end: 'Then the evildoers will no longer exist!' As soon as sin disappears, there will be no more evildoers. So pray *for* them, so that they turn back in repentance, then there will be no more evildoers." Then he prayed for mercy for them, and in fact they repented [Ber 10a].

This is the wisdom of the Talmudic teachers who combat evil but try to win the evildoer over.

For all those other religious heroes—in Judaism and elswhere—who succeeded in praying for their persecutors, their enemies, even their torturers, the Polish philosopher Leszek Kolakowski can speak:

> The religious tradition, at least in our cultural circle, demands more than the mere challenge to renounce hate; beyond this we should show our persecutors kindness, pray for our enemy. Must a claim so offensive to nature be considered universally binding? The answer can be only the most banal: certainly there are and will be in the future only a very few who are really equal to this summons; but on the shoulders of these few rests the structure of our civilization, and we ordinary ones, insofar as we are able, are grateful to them.[33]

Yet Kolakowski errs if he thinks Jesus' demands that we renounce hate and love our enemy originate solely in a self-denial that has only our adversary's well-being at heart. The point here is really a double bridge, one between our world of violence and the reign of heaven on earth, and the other between a legitimate self-interest and enlightened altruism.

That the Nazarene did not see it as a question of an enthusiastic self-surrender contradicting the biblical idea of human dignity and the ethos of scripture, but rather as a mutual dismantling of hostility by a vigorous reconciliation benefiting the hater as well as the hated is shown by the two concrete examples that Jesus gives as illustrations. But first we must outline the political background and the human climate of that age in which Jesus first saw the light of day.

It was a gloomy light and a dreadful day—full of panic, terror, and anxiety—at the time of that first Roman tax extortion, which Jewish writings of those dark times refer to tersely as "sucking the land dry." The much-touted *pax romana* was the tyrannic rule of a Roman occupational force that threatened to break the people down by its arrogant arbitrariness, shameless corruption, and brutal violation of law. The occupiers' heavy financial demands on the people were especially crushing: eleven different taxes, tariffs, and assessments that the despot had his Jewish puppets, the notorious tax collectors, round up. No wonder that these "stooges" were so deeply hated by the people as collaborators and betrayers.

Also on the side of the authorities were the great landowners, for the most part Jewish minions of the Romans, who, with the help of a corrupt judiciary, could cheaply buy up or expropriate the family holdings of small farmers deep in debt and often lease them back to their former owners, degrading them by inflated rents to the status of day laborers or serfs.

Other allies of the Roman authorities were the Sadducees, that little group of the Jerusalem priestly aristocracy who knew how to adapt to the brutal regime in order to defend their corner of power. The fact that in this they passively put up with and actively supported the exploitation of the people contributed considerably to their reputation as quislings.

Under the pressure of an acute Jewish eschatological expectation and the scourge of this triple oppressive front, the situation came repeatedly to open insurrection, in which Roman force, popular revolt, and religious impatience again and again solidified into a vicious circle that exacted a high toll in blood. Any Jew who has lived in a country occupied by the enemy can empathize with the historical circumstances in Jesus' homeland during his lifetime.

ZEALOTS AND SADDUCEES

All of Israel fell at that time into three groupings that as such had nothing to do with political or religious ties: the mass of the despondent, for whom naked survival in a time of need became the chief goal; the deserters who squandered their biblical right of inheritance for a mess of pottage at the table of the powerful; and the resolute, for whom a life without justice and freedom was meaningless. No one who can picture this tripartite division will have any doubt which group a man of the Nazarene's stature belonged to.

"Fanatics"—"zealots" in Greek—was the name taken by the leaders of those who in God's name stirred up the "mandatory war" against the pagan yoke in order to liberate their people from the hated Romans and their despised sycophants and accomplices. At bottom, just about all Jews of that day were zealots for God and the reign of God. Individual groups differed among themselves only in their methods and the portion of the work of redemption that they were willing to cede to God.

Passivists wished to hasten the day of the Lord by prayer and loyalty to the Torah. Activists set about with fire, sword, and guerilla warfare to drive out force with counterforce in order to usher in the fervently desired reign of heaven.

Each day the confession "Hear, O Israel" (Deut. 6:4), which makes absolute love of God the highest commandment, was recited with great ardor by members of all three groupings. In the exegesis of love of neighbor, however, they were of various opinions.

The Sadducee elite gave the *reya'* in the commandment of love of neighbor (Lev. 19:18) the restricted sense of "friend" or "compatriot." The Zealots made loyalty to the Torah and militant patriotism the precondition for being a neighbor. With an appeal to King David who had said, "I hate, Lord, those who hate you. . . . They have become my enemy" (Ps. 139:21ff.), they marched forward in their divine zeal over the bodies of Romans and disloyal Jews.

Jesus was certainly no Zealot, no revolutionary in the usual sense, not even a Galilean gang leader. His statements against violence as a political combat method are too numerous for this to be doubted seriously. But one who can say, "I have not come to bring peace but the sword" (Matt. 10:34), and who advises his disciples to sell their cloaks "so that they can buy a sword" (Luke 22:36), is just as unlikely to be an outright pacifist. It is also clear that certainly one, but probably three and perhaps even five of the twelve apostles had a Zealot background. They are Simon, who is twice named "the Zealot" by Luke (Acts 1:13; Luke 6:15; cf. Matt. 10:4); Judas Iscariot, whose surname is an Aramaic corruption of "dagger-man" (*sicarius*), as the hard core of Zealots were then called; Simon Peter, whose other name, Bar-Jonah, may be an Aramaic synonym for "rebel" or "ostracized"; and the two sons of Zebedee who, with their nickname "Sons of Thunder," do not exactly give the impression of having forsworn armed service, all the more because their sole appearance in the New Testament is dominated by their angry words: "Lord, do you wish that we order fire to fall from heaven and consume these Samaritans?" (Luke 9:54).

It is thus evident from a historical perspective that Jesus could not have been completely out of contact with the militant activists in contemporaneous Israel.

Of Jesus' many references to swords, none of which advocate folding one's hands in resignation, one is outstanding for two good reasons: because it is the only saying that is mentioned five times in the Gospels, and because something like it is also found in a Jewish tradition of that time, where it is cited as a Zealot saying. "Only the one who is prepared to carry the cross shall follow after me," we read in Mark (8:34), twice in Matthew (10:38; 16:24), and twice in Luke (9:23; 14:27).

Much later the church fathers spiritualized and defused this summons into an otherworldly appeal to personal salvation. What it signified when Jesus said it on earth was much simpler, more challenging, and deadly in earnest. It was a well-intended warning to young hotheads in Galilee who wanted to join his movement in the flush of their enthusiasm. To them he said: whoever of you is not prepared to risk the possible consequences, the rebel's death on a Roman cross, stay home. It was the gruesome, brutal truth: thousands of Jews before Jesus, with Jesus, on both sides of Jesus, and after Jesus were put to death by crucifixion.

Even non-Zealots who merely showed interest in opposition or dared to voice political criticism of Roman imperialism had to reckon with this consequence. The Twelve understood this when they left home and property behind them without looking back in order to fight for Israel with their master—for better or for worse.

"Yes," some Christians may object, "but Jesus did say, my kingdom is not of this world." In Greek and in English Jesus' statement may sound like a summons to flee the world, to postpone all that is good, beautiful, and noble into the hereafter, and to abandon this world to despots, dictators, and tyrants.

But translated back into Hebrew it signifies the exact opposite: my realm, which we all await so passionately, is of heavenly origin and divine descent—unlike the Roman empire of idol-worshipers. It will soon be inaugurated in this world to replace all the horror of pagan power and in the end to entrust dominion to God alone.

"My realm is not of this world." This saying was politically no less loaded with dynamite than the themes of "good news," "redemption," and "realm of heaven," which Jesus preached day after day and which resonated with revolt and liberation in all Jewish ears of that time. This could not be otherwise, because for faithful Jews God's omnipresence must logically also include the sphere of politics, a belief clearly exemplified in all the prophets of Israel. In bringing about the reign of God, exclusion of the political would therefore be an almost blasphemous denial of the divinely-willed world order.

The later depoliticizing of Christianity, on the other hand, split this world into two clearly distinct realms in order to defend the church from all defilement by worldly concerns, and, in contradiction to Jesus and his scripture, succeeded in surrendering the earth, allowing it to become an arena for dictators.

For the Jew Jesus, on the other hand, there was no cleft between body and spirit, between religion and politics, no bifurcation of competencies, but only *one* total person under the *one* God and *one* dream of an all-encompassing heavenly realm.

JESUS' THIRD WAY

Just as corporeality and concern for physical well-being are not to be separated from his Instruction on the Mount, politics cannot be amputated from his good news. Liberation from the pagan yoke, redemption from faintheartedness, and boundless love of

God and fellow humans—these are the three chief goals of his salvation teaching, which he, as a practical-minded Jew, knew could not be realized on this earth without down-to-earth methods. For if the eschatological peace-vision is to be prepared in an earthly manner—though of course with heavenly authority—then humans as God's collaborators must make use of political means to make it concrete. Moses knew that on Sinai; all the prophets of Israel knew it—and so did Jesus of Nazareth, who never wished to give unto Caesar what belongs to God alone.[34]

Martin Luther was right in his polemic against the rebellious peasants and Pastor Thomas Münzer when he characterized the urge for freedom as "Jewish." It is not by chance that the body of faith of all Christian freedom fighters—from the Cathari of southern France, the Waldensians of Piedmont, the Hussites of Prague, the Puritans in England, and the Pilgrims in North America, to the Maoris of New Zealand, the black churches of contemporary South Africa, and the *campesinos* of Latin America—is permeated with the language and turn of mind of the Book of Exodus, that hymn of God-given freedom. And Jesus of Nazareth, who in all the physical and spiritual characteristics of his humanity was totally a Jew, an arch-Jew, is never more Jewish than in his opposition to subjugation, whether it be enslavement to the literal faith of the priestly caste or oppression by the brutal Roman authorities and their Jewish camp followers who exploited his people godlessly and shamelessly.

But above all he was a threefold rebel of love, much more radical than revolutionaries of our day. He dared, without weapons, to protest against the cruel Roman domination; he opposed the high clergy of the Sadducees who assumed in their narrow-mindedness that they had a monopoly on God's love; and at the same time he raised an eloquent protest against the faintheartedness of many of his compatriots who would not credit the God of Abraham, Isaac, and Jacob with a salvation politics of liberation.

And yet Jesus was against naked armed force—neither out of unworldliness nor out of cowardice, but out of biblical farsightedness and realistic worldly experience. Between the quietism of the silent majority and the fanaticism of the despairing minority Jesus found a third way—the golden mean—which promised that "the meek will possess the land," as both the Psalter and the Instruction on the Mount foretell (Matt. 5:5; Ps. 38:11). "Not with power nor with force, but by the spirit of the Lord," preached the prophet Zechariah (4:6). Jesus did not want it otherwise.

"One of those accompanying Jesus drew his sword," we read at the capture in Gethsemani; but Jesus said to him, "Put your sword in its scabbard, for all those who draw the sword will die by the sword" (Matt. 26:51–52).

"Lord, see, here are two swords!" the disciples urged him. "But he said to them: That is enough!" (Luke 22:38).

"Lord, shall we smite them with the sword?" the foolhardy nevertheless asked. "But Jesus said: Stop! No further!" (Luke 22:49f.).

Jesus' third way relied neither on passive powerlessness nor on militant counterforce, but on a completely new course of human interaction that would invert all dominant relationships and deprive them of power:

> You know that those who are considered the rulers of the gentiles oppress their peoples and that their great men tyrannize them. But it must not be so among you. Whoever among you will be great should be your servant, and whoever among you would be the first should be the servant of all [Mark 10:42–45].

How such an ethos of equality, of comradely service and disarming love, should be modeled by the community of disciples amid a brutal world full of ogres grabbing for power and getting the upperhand was illustrated by Jesus with two straightforward examples from the everyday life of that time, to be taken up in the following chapter.

Chapter 11

JEWISH CREDITORS AND ROMAN TASKMASTERS
(Matt. 5:40–41)

TUNIC AND CLOAK

If someone wishes to take you to court to take your tunic away from you, then let him also have your cloak [Matt. 5:40].

The reference here is to indebted day laborers, to mortgage law, and the protective provisions for those who lived from hand to mouth, those whom Jesus' Bible intends to defend from the "justice" of the state. The pronouncement has to do with a legal renunciation that at first seems to border on the paradoxical but is calculated to achieve beneficial results.

But first to the biblical background of this unheard-of precept. Both Deuteronomy and Exodus hand down the text of the Ten Commandments (Exod. 20:2–17; Deut. 5:6–21) as the "fundamental law" revealed immediately by God for the people. The decalogue is then followed in both instances by individual rules intended to make this fundamental law, which is valid always and everywhere, concrete and actual for sundry situations. This is illustrated particularly by Exodus 22:20–27, consisting of two parallel passages in which God puts order into and shapes communal life. In the first (vv. 22–23) the text shows clearly that God will not put up with violation of the rights of the weak and the defenseless.

Not to be overlooked is the degree to which both parts are influenced by the Israelite experience of slavery and the divine liberation from Egypt. This is shown not only in the motivation given at the very beginning ("For you were yourselves strangers in Egypt and have discovered in your own body what oppression and exploitation in a foreign country mean"), but especially in the repeated "cry of the oppressed" (vv. 22 and 27) that is "heard by God." This is the basic structure of the exodus story and, in fact, the Jewish credo in general (cf. Deut. 26:5–10). Where the right to life of humans is concerned, God is affected, "for I have compassion" (v. 27). Where the life of the poor and defenseless is at stake, the exodus established once and for all that the God of Israel is the God of the lowly, those who are most in need of God.

The consequences, therefore, must not be limited to the area of abstract morality but must also obligate juridically. Wherever human rights are violated, the divine enterprise is at stake.

In the second part (Exod. 22:24–27), the example of the relevant laws on interest and pledges says even more trenchantly that the claims of certain rights find their God-given limits wherever the question of human dignity enters the lives of the poor. Those who are so poor or so in debt that they are threatened in their human dignity or in their social existence, should be lent money without any demand for legally permitted interest, because they are "of my people."

The same is true for those whose debts are greater than all their assets except for the "shirt on their back"—a clear case where right and righteousness collide. How the two ought to be reconciled is recorded very clearly for the narrow-minded literalist: "If you take the cloak of your neighbor as pledge, you are to return it before the sun goes down, for his cloak is his only covering for his body; how else should he sleep?" (Exod. 22:26).

The fifth book of Moses speaks in this same vein:

> If you lend something to your neighbor, you should not go into his house and take a pledge from him, but you should stand outside and he to whom you lend should bring his pledge out to you. But if he is poor, you should not lie down to sleep with his pledge but should return his pledge to him

when the sun sets so that he may sleep in his cloak and bless you [Deut. 24:10ff.].

In their efforts to preclude any possible exploitation of the poor, the rabbis went a step further:

Before the sun goes down you should give it back to him (Exod. 22:26)—that refers to his night garment [i.e., the cloak, on which the poor slept]; you should give back the pledge when the sun sets (Deut. 24:13)—this refers to his daytime garment: that is, his tunic or his undergarment [Baba Metzia 114b].

The needy must thus in no case be left exposed, even if their debts are so great that a pledge of clothing is justified. In extremity it is not the law that holds but God's righteousness, which gives grace precedence over justice.

In the words of the Bible, "Do what is *right and good* in the eyes of the Eternal One, so that it will go well with you" (Deut. 6:18). Rashi, the great biblical commentator of the Jewish Middle Ages, explains this verse as a command to come to terms with one's opponent in legal cases in a fair compromise, and not to persist in carrying out a legal claim in full.

The rabbis coined an expression for this behavior, that one *lifnim mi-shurat ha-din*—that is, one should move out beyond the hard borders of legal prescriptions. Put simply, this means renouncing rights; voluntarily assuming a more stringent interpretation of a commandment for oneself; going beyond the obligatory norm; easing demands on one's neighbor; avoiding boastfulness; acting "for heaven's sake"; working for the common good—all that Matthew characterizes in the Instruction on the Mount as "the better righteousness" (Matt. 5:20), but which his Lord and Master demands in Hebrew as "within the legal line."

As an example, the following is reported in the Talmud (BM 83a). Rabbi Barbar Hana had commissioned two porters to bring some wine to his house. Through carelessness the barrel fell to the ground and smashed. In his anger over the losses he sustained, Barbar Hana seized the garments of the bearers, who then complained to the famous scholar Rav.

Rav called upon Barbar Hana to return their garments to the porters, and when the injured man asked whether he had no claim to compensation, he was informed, "You should take the way of the good" (Prov. 2:20). When the porters had received their clothing back, they complained that they had labored an entire day, were hungry, and were left destitute. At this, Rav sentenced the employer to pay the customary daily wage, and to his objection that according to the law he was not obligated to this, Rav answered with Solomon's counsel: "And you shall keep on the path of the righteous" (Prov. 2:20).

The employer in this case was a well-known rabbi whose integrity no one doubted. Nevertheless he had to be told that in his lawsuit with the day laborers he must not press his "legitimate claims" to the full, for in that case what was *right* would not be *good*.

Certainly not all employers of that time—or ours—were so understanding and so prepared to submit to such an adverse judgment without protest. In fact, the very prominence given this episode in the Talmud strengthens the suspicion that we have here a praiseworthy exception that is held up as a model precisely because it seems to pillory the deplorable way most employers insisted on their rights.

It was to such "normal cases" that Jesus seems to refer, although it is the poor day laborers whom he calls on to renounce their biblical minimum rights. Does that not contradict all earthly logic and all human ideas of righteousness? And why does Jesus not turn, as would be proper and fair, to the affluent employer, as Rav did in the Talmud passage, to persuade him to renounce his right to the poor man's tunic? It was, after all, a tunic that might indeed belong to him legally, but without which he nevertheless could do quite nicely!

The answer to this question we find in the episode of the rich young man—the story of precluded discipleship. Here we are told of what was surely not an infrequent occurrence in the course of Jesus' travels:

> Then one came to him and asked him, "Rabbi, what good deed shall I do in order to attain eternal life?" Jesus answered him, "Why do you ask me about what is good? One alone is good. If you wish to enter into eternal life, keep the

commandments." "Which?" he said. Jesus answered, "These: you shall not kill, not commit adultery, not steal, not bear false witness, honor your father and your mother, and love your neighbor as yourself." The young man answered him, "All these I have kept. What is lacking?" Jesus answered him, "If you will be blameless, go and sell your property and give it to the poor, then you will have treasure in heaven. Then come and follow me." When the young man heard this he went away sad, for he had great possessions [Matt. 19:16–22].

The rich young man must have been very devout: he said he observed all God's commandments carefully—an assertion acknowledged by Jesus without a trace of skepticism. Precisely for that reason Jesus thought him capable of giving up his possessions for the sake of the poor, an extraordinary demand that no doubt today would meet with the same "sad" refusal as then.

The young man was certainly prepared for charity, alms, and tithing for the poor, but "sell your property and give it to the poor" was more than he—and all of his kind—were prepared to take on. After several such attempts, which must have been just as unsuccessful, Jesus apparently gave up on the rich as "servants of mammon." With a sigh of resignation he observed, "It is easier for a camel to go through the eye of a needle than for a rich person to enter the realm of God" (Matt. 19:24). Henceforth he turned his attention to the poor, his principal concern all his life. But in this instance he seems not to have been intent on their welfare, for he advises debtors to renounce their rights, though they are in danger of losing their last possession.

Actually we should say their second-last possession, for even the poor as a rule had at least two garments, as Jesus himself made clear when he sent forth his twelve disciples, who certainly did not belong to the well-to-do class. "Do not take gold or silver or copper coins in your belt, or a travel bag or *two* tunics, neither shoes nor staff. For the worker is deserving of his pay" (Matt. 10:9).

Nevertheless it must still be explained why Jesus ventured to make a demand of the poor so extreme that it is written off by many exegetes as "absurd" or "purely symbolic."

One possible answer to this question would be that Jesus, who called the poor blessed (Luke 6:20; Matt. 5:3), believed that being poor drove a person to expect everything from God alone, a precondition to entering the realm of heaven. Or that he expected God's passionately awaited royal dominion to reverse the wretched fate of all the poor. If Jesus understood himself as the one sent by God and anointed with the Spirit "to bring good news to the poor" (Isa. 61:1), as he proclaimed in the synagogue at Nazareth (Luke 4:16ff.), then he may also have acted out the mandate (Isa. 11:4) to demand, as judge of the poor and wretched in the land, spiritual greatness of these marginal members of society, to hasten by their renunciation of rights the approach of redemptive *sedakah*.

It may be that Jesus thought of the orientations to private property expressed in the following judgment of the rabbis:

> There is a fourfold opinion on the basic question of mine and yours. The one who says what is mine is mine and what is yours is yours is among the mediocre. Some say this is the manner of Sodom. The one who says what is mine is yours and what is yours is mine acts according to the way of those ignorant of Torah. The one who says what is yours is mine and what is mine is mine is a transgressor. But the one who says what is mine is yours and what is yours is yours—that is the truly pious [Another version reads: that is the manner of the holy] [Aboth V, 10].

Here renouncing possessions is extolled as a virtue and elevated to an ideal, though one that only very few persons have ever been able to follow. Calvin surely speaks here for most Jews and Christians when he says of Matthew 5:40: "It would be absurd to insist on the words; . . . it would be better to take one's opponent to court" (*Evangelienharmonie*, I, 196).

Not to be excluded is still another explanation, one that would be tantamount to a concretization of Jesus' general advice to his disciples "to be mild as doves and wise as serpents" (Matt. 10:16) in order to latch onto a bit of good fortune on earth through shrewd humility.

The text seems to corroborate this assumption, for Jesus does *not* say, "*Give* him your cloak also," but "Let him," or, in Hebrew, "Permit him your cloak as well'—which amounts to an offer made in the hope of a refusal on the part of the plaintiff. It is not an unconditional surrender of the cloak, which would deprive the creditor of the opportunity to prove himself high-minded and generous before the judge.

Likewise Jesus did *not* say, "*Ask* your opponent for a second box on the ear," but "Turn the other cheek" (Mark 5:39)—in the same hope that the opponent would not attack a second time. In neither case does Jesus in any way abandon his ground of magnanimous realism.

This would also correspond to the gesture of submission by the defeated with which, according to contemporary research on aggression, most duels among animals of the same species end.

Many things speak for the fact that the generosity of an inferior can move even brutal debt collectors to a sense of shame, which, perhaps with the help of a judge, may help them to insight. Certainly the surprise of the weaker party's advancing halfway would give rise to more forebearance and consideration than would persistent hammering on a biblical privilege that runs counter to a financial claim sanctioned by law. That Jesus, thanks to this method of disarming compliance, seems to reckon with the plaintiff's renunciation of the offered cloak is demonstrated by his famous statement directed to these same twelve apostles: "If someone has no sword, let him sell his cloak and buy one" (Luke 22:36).

In any case this explanation accords both with the first Beatitude and with the messianic hope that God "fills the hungry with good things and sends the rich home empty" (Luke 1:53). For none of the prophetic expectations of the future in Judaism is inconsistent with the independent exertions of the poor to ease their difficult earthly lot in an honorable way—or the frequently emphasized endeavor to be practical "collaborators of God" in the work of saving this world.

THE SECOND MILE

Just as the first example of Jesus' illustration of disarming love is connected with Jewish exploiters, so the second logically concerns the Roman subjugators—the two groups that made life bitter for the poor in Israel.

If someone forces you to go a mile with him, go two [Matt. 5:41].

The topic here is of course the infamous *angareia*—the compulsory service of the Romans (as *milion*, a Greek loanword, makes clear), which permitted any legionary to load his bag and baggage on any Jew passing by (Simon of Cyrene in Mark 15:21) and use him as a beast of burden for one mile. At the end of this stretch the Jew was permitted to throw the baggage at the feet of the tyrant and flee—that is, if he had not run off beforehand, a practice often avenged with draconian penalties. In either case, mutual enmity was strengthened, so that every day supplied further fuel for the increasing rebellion of the people and the bloody reprisals of the occupiers.

Jesus suggests a third course of action: transforming compulsory service into a voluntary escort after the prescribed mile so that the astounded Roman would be disarmed—in the best sense of the word—by graciousness.

Here the initiative is taken away from the superior, evil is repaid with good, and, in all probability, in the course of the second mile a friendly conversation will begin to develop. For, as the words of the prophet, which Jesus may have had in mind, attest, "Can two persons walk along together without being in accord on the way?" (Amos 3:3).

That such a disarming love—both in this question of escort and in the matter of clothing and care—was not only preached but actually practiced here and there is shown in the following midrash, which comes out of those difficult times:

> Once there was a shipwrecked Roman who, in the time of the heaviest Roman yoke, was washed up naked on the shore of the land of Israel. He hid himself under some rocks and called out from there to a group of Jewish festival pilgrims, "I am a descendant of Esau, your brother. Give me something to wear to cover my bareness, for the sea has stripped me, and I was able to rescue nothing!" They answered him, "May your entire people be stripped!"
>
> Then that Roman raised his eyes, saw Rabbi Eleazar who was walking among them, and called, "I see that you are an old man, honored by your people. You show due respect to

creatures, so help me!" Rabbi Eleazar ben Shammua owned several garments. He took one of them and gave it to the man. He also led him into his house, provided him with food and drink, gave him two hundred denarii, accompanied him for fourteen miles, and showed him great honor, until he had brought the Roman to his house [Midrash Eccl. Rabba 11, 1].

Chapter 12

TAX-COLLECTOR ETHIC AND GENEROSITY ETHIC (Matt. 5:46–48)

Jesus was not concerned with isolated instances of exemplary deeds, but with a new code of deportment for the masses of the eternally inferior, whom he hoped to make collaborators in the pacification of Israel through their own reorientation. In other words, he called upon his disciples to make a beginning in the form of a unilateral prepayment on credit, so to speak, in order to burst the ancient vicious circle of hate and counterhate, of violence and counterviolence.

Just take the first step, is his appeal. Just as God began with love in creating you capable of love, imitate God and quickly take the first step toward the loveless! Perhaps you can change them by a meaningful gesture. Perhaps they have known so little love that they have forgotten how to love and only await your loving initiative to become fellow human beings once again. Give it a try! All you have to lose is a half hour of footwork, but you might gain a helper, a well-wisher, even a friend!

Jesus demands neither expressions of sympathy nor declarations of love; he does not ask that we renounce power, only that we foster peaceable reconciliation in a reasonable way. Unconditional self-surrender, however, can never be called reasonable, contradicting as it would the sober-minded words that Jesus directed to these same disciples: "Whoever has no sword . . . let him sell his cloak and buy one. . . . But they said, 'Lord, see, here are two swords!' But he said, 'It is enough' " (Luke 22:35–36). In plain words, it as much as says that at least two of the disciples had anticipated Jesus' advice and were already armed—and also that Jesus subsequently approved this.

Two swords among thirteen men are of course sufficient only for self-defense, but in occupied Palestine of the first century it was accounted an extremely suspicious illegality. Roman law severely forbade the Jews (except for a privileged few) to bear swords. Violators were frequently treated as rebels and crucified.

Thus Jesus was prepared to obey the dictates of reasonable self-defense, even in dangerous contradiction to the stipulations of the pagan occupation force. Paul, who in chapter 12 of his Letter to the Romans presents a kind of abridged version of the Instruction on the Mount, seems to have understood his Lord correctly when he writes, "If possible, to the extent that it depends on you, live in peace with everyone" (Rom. 12:18). The first two phrases are unambiguously intended as much against passive surrender as against keeping oneself out of unavoidable conflicts.

When Bishop Lohse correctly emphasizes that "we could not have the Sermon on the Mount without the preacher on the mount," it also means that Jesus' teaching must be grasped in its entirety to do him justice—a teaching that cannot be reduced to a thumbnail sketch, because it encompasses his entire life and ministry, all his efforts to teach and convert, of which the Instruction on the Mount portrays only a fraction.

But now back to Jesus' disarming love, which Luke mentions twice in his parallel sermon on the plain (Luke 6:27, 35)—both times in the radical sense of "do good to those who hate you" but in no way as unlimited self-denial.

There had been a rabbinic debate over the priority between two biblical precepts that in certain circumstances could give rise to a quandary. Its solution sprang from this same concern for reasonableness.

In the fifth book of Moses we read, "If you see your brother's donkey or ox fall, you should take it upon yourself to help" (Deut. 22:4). The second book of Moses says, "If you see your hater's donkey sink under its burden, then don't leave him in the lurch, but work together with him to raise the animal" (Exod. 23:5).

But what should one do, the question arises, in a case where your brother's donkey and your hater's donkey need your assistance at precisely the same time? The answer, which Jesus surely knew, went: First help your hater's donkey, for in doing that you not only save an animal but also touch the heart of your opponent and gain a friend. Only then go and help your brother's donkey. Three acts of kindness in one sweep!

The midrash on Psalm 99:4 is a good example of enlivening dry principles with the flesh and blood of parable:

> A man goes on his way and sees his hater's donkey collapse under its burden. He goes over, puts out his hand, and helps him first to unload and then to reload. Afterward they go into an inn and the owner of the donkey—even if he is a pagan— says in his heart: "The so-and-so does like me, and I wrongly thought he hated me." At once they talk together and make peace.

In brief, Jesus advocates reaching out a helping hand to someone who does not like you and is in need.

It is just this practical method of disarming, which has nothing to do with extremism or superhuman quality, that Jesus proposes as a biblical realpolitik designed to deflate conflicts with either a foreign ruler or a local tyrant, to turn adversaries into good neighbors at least and real friends if possible. But a disarming love has two facets to it: change those around you and change yourself! Change them so that they rid themselves of hate and by their new relationship to you can also change you for the better. It is those who know how to love themselves and others who know how to defuse hate.

The fact that Jesus calls enemies "haters" (as the Lukan parallel 6:27 insinuates) and avoids the word "enemy" in his gospel suggests another dimension. "Enemy" in most languages connotes a deep-seated opposition, whereas "hater" is a noun derived from a verb and like all verbs has a temporary quality about it and thus implicitly hints at its own termination. From time immemorial, opposing sides have been prepared for war by a friend-and-enemy attitude that strengthens fear of another people or nation by fantasizing all possible evil in them until they become the very incarnation of all that is inhuman, and using any means against them becomes legitimate. Fear easily gives way to hatred, a hatred that, thanks to simplistic painting in black and white, can even assume the halo of a "just war," for against the devil anything is permitted. This is the way it happened with Cain, with Amalek, with Haman, with the Zealots—and with Hitler.

Jesus would nip this escalation in the bud by admitting that enemies, as (convertible) "haters," are human beings in whom enough good characteristics can be discovered to justify the hope of disarming them. Thus the hater and the hated remain within the sphere of the human, which of course includes an enormous range of variety but no contrasts so extreme as to be unbridgeable.

And so Jesus teaches:

> Show those that hate you acts of kindness and pray for those who persecute you, so that you may become offspring of your Father in heaven [Matt. 5:45].

"Become," it says here, in good Hebraic style; for Jewish sonship of God is, unlike the Greek, not a privilege of birth, but must be earned and achieved by God-pleasing deeds—among which the service of peace enjoys a high preeminence. It must be added here once again that the Hebrew word for "offspring" (*banim*) is in no way limited to male descendants but in the context of that day can mean successor, follower, heir, supporter, or emulator.

This is clearly a matter of the imitation of God in the sense of a the theo-politics of imaginative and loving effort for peace; just as obviously, it concerns the same divine sonship or daughtership that the seventh Beatitude emphatically links to one and the same strategy of reconciliation: "Blessed are the peacemakers, for they will be called sons of God" (Matt 5:9).

"Peacemaker" and "All-Merciful" are frequent synonyms for God in the Hebrew liturgy, which elevates both characteristics to principal attributes of God. Indeed our heavenly Father lives them out before us day after day: God "lets the sun rise on the evil and the good, and lets rain fall on the just and the unjust" (Matt. 5:45).

Anyone who can imitate such boundless love—even if only in approximate measure—in order to actualize the shalom that God wills for the earth will be ennobled with the poetic honorary title of "son (or daughter) of God."

As Jesus uses this Hebrew term, it is an arduous process, full of self-denial, to become a "son of God" in the rabbinic meaning of that term—the final goal of human endeavor. It seems, then, that the conclusion of the series of "supertheses" is incorrectly translated "You ought to be perfect as your Father in heaven is perfect" (Matt. 5:48). This seems not only an exorbitant demand, humanly impossible and foreign to all Jesus' realism, but also an entirely superfluous repetition of the basic thought of the imitation of God already expressed so eloquently in Matthew 5:9 and 5:45.

In a Semitic coinage, however, the Greek word *teleios* has the sense of wholeness—the opposite of conflict, which houses "two spirits in its breast" and is therefore discordant within itself. This concept of wholeness *(shalem)* is included in *shalom,* which implies a three-dimensional wholeness—with the self, with God, and with the surrounding world—as an all-encompassing harmony of unity that corresponds to the demand for impeccability and purity of heart. Noah, Abraham, and Job did justice to it, because they were precisely what an entire, undivided person can and should be. This unrestricted, unbroken wholeness demands one's entire heart and total behavior, so that conviction and conduct are hewed out of a single stone, precluding schizophrenia. Integral wholeness of the entire potential of human nature is thus seen as a realizable challenge.

Full being-with-God demands an unconditional orientation to God instead of to the world and its halfway measures. It rivets its eye on the highest goal as it makes God's holiness and love the measure of its own conduct, not in order to become a showcase of all virtue but rather in full consciousness of human inadequacy.

"You should be perfect" can be understood in the Qumran tradition as the total actualization of the commandment "You should be holy for I your God am holy" (Lev. 19:2). For normative Judaism, on the other hand, a breath of blasphemy can almost be heard here, for "all have sinned" (1 Kings 8:46); "all have strayed, for there is no one who does good" (Ps. 14:1–3) and "no flesh can endure before God" (Isa. 40:6). "Perfection " is a divine attribute, not applicable to mortals. In the words of Leo Baeck:

Since complete fulfillment of the command to be holy even as is God is impossible, the claim of having done even more than

necessary is absurd. Jewish teaching and prayer reiterate that
before God there is no merit. Striving and struggling human
beings we can be; but we are never complete or perfect.[35]

"Be (humanly) whole as your Father in heaven is (divinely)
whole" is thus a better translation, linking together the fulfillment
of all the commandments of love, both as the full realization of
human potential and, secondarily, as the imitation of God, two
distinct wholenesses.

There is also another possibility: to trace *teleios* back to its
probable origin in a way that is true to the context and general
sense. A retranslation from Matthew 5:48 to the Aramaic (or to
Qumran Hebrew) yields a verb form *t-sh-l-mun,* which, with vowels supplied, can be read either as "be perfect" *(tishlemun)* or as
"repay" *(teshalmun).* The complete context as well as the struc-
turing of Jesus' discourse are closer to the second reading: "You
should recompense as your heavenly Father recompenses." And
for this reading "neither a dot nor a stroke" of the text has to be
changed.

This meaning—repay evil with good, curse with blessing, hate
with love, as does God—can be considered the most apt resumé of
the excerpt on the boundlessness of all love (Matt. 5:43–48). This
reading also harmonizes much better with the Lukan parallel,
which basically says the same thing, "Be merciful as your Father is
merciful" (Luke 6:36).

Not to be overlooked is the fact that this fundamental idea that
humans should recompense as God does—in fact that the two
"recompenses" have an almost causal connection—runs like a
crimson thread through Jesus' entire kerygmatic:

"Judge not so that you will not be judged" (Matt 7:1).

"Condemn not and you will not be condemned" (Luke 6:37).

"With the measure with which you measure it will be measured
for you" (Luke 6:38).

"Give, and it will be given to you." (Luke: 6:38).

"Blessed are the merciful, for they will be 'mercied' " (Matt.
5:7).

The *passivum divinum* is a reverent paraphrase for God the
Recompenser. It parallels the petition in the Our Father: "Forgive
us our debts, as we also have forgiven our debtors" (Matt. 6:12).

Jesus says it a seventh time: "If you forgive others their lapses, then your heavenly Father will also forgive you. But if you do not forgive others, your Father will also not forgive you your lapses" (Matt. 6:14f.).

To sum up: you should repay as your Father in heaven repays. That once again corresponds to an old Jewish teaching, as Jesus ben Sirach noted almost two centuries before the birth of the Nazarene, "The Lord avenges himself on whoever practices vengeance, and remembers his sins. If you forgive your neighbor an injustice, then you, when you pray, will also be forgiven your sins" (Sir. 28:1-2). Or, still clearer and closer to Jesus' meaning, "God speaks: Be like me—just as I recompense evil with good, so you too should repay evil with good" (Ex Rabba 26:2).

The very human "tax-collector ethic" (Matt. 5:46), which loves only benefactors and computes gifts and return gifts with mathematical precision, is superseded by a "generosity ethic," which joins sympathy to magnanimity, aware that your needy fellow humans, even if they are angry with you, are still God's creatures, and as such have a divinely-willed right to your assistance.

Numerous citations from rabbinic writings affirm that it is not only God's inexhaustible, gracious love that is presented for imitation but also God's gentle pedagogy aimed at moving the hater, sinner, and blasphemer to insight and conversion through kindness. Jesus can therefore have presumed this as common knowledge.

The goal and purpose of the imitation of God is, in the last analysis, to build a bridge between enlightened self-interest and farsighted altruism, between legitimate self-love and biblical love of neighbor—for we are told, "Love your neighbor *as yourself*—and simultaneously between the real world of today and the heavenly realm of tomorrow.

In the words of the first-century Jewish *Didache*, which reads like a pragmatic commentary on the Instruction on the Mount, "What kind of thanks do you get if you love those who love you? Don't the heathens do that? But love those who hate you; then you will have no enemies" (1:3).

Chapter 13

THE OTHER CHEEK
(Matt. 5:39b)

The same calm and sober idealism with which Jesus links the
Golden Rule (Matt. 7:12) with the mandate to be both "gentle as
doves" and "wise as serpents" (Matt. 10:16) also animates the third
climactic statement of the Instruction on the Mount:

If someone slaps you on the right cheek, turn the other to him also"
[Matt. 5:39b].

The first thing to be noted here is that this is not a normal
occurrence, because only left-handed persons hit the right cheek of
someone facing them. As Jesus was doubtless aware of this, we
must dig deeper to understand what he means.

Talmudic discussion on compensation in the case of bodily injury is helpful here. We read:

If someone gives his neighbor a box on the ear . . . , then he
pays 200 sus as reparation. . . . But should it be with the
hand turned—that is, with the back of the hand—then he
pays 400 sus. Why double? The slap with the back of the hand
certainly hurts less, but it is accounted a gesture of contempt,
which inflicts greater insult and doubly insults and affronts
[Baba Kamma 8, 6, and T Baba Kamma 31].

Jesus is thus not speaking only of slaps that hurt but of a
deliberate insult joining pain and humiliation. A Jew not acting out

121

of sudden anger would surely take care not to "slap the other cheek," for if he should injure his victim (even the smallest bleeding wound counts), he has five payments to make: for damages, pain, medical expenses, time lost, and loss of face (Mishna Baba Kamma BK VIII, 1; cf. Kethuboth 33a).

As with many of Jesus' statements, we are dealing here with an ambiguity that can scarcely be reduced to a common denominator. At least five different explanations are known to theology.

POSSIBLE EXPLANATIONS

This is a matter, say the rigorists, of consciously demanding far too much of oneself, of a mandate that virtually transcends all human moral power in demanding total renunciation of one's own dignity for the sake of total love of neighbor.

But it could also be an ethic of self-abasement, a second school believes, which would subdue normal egoism by deliberate humiliation, or even halt it before it develops. This may seem radical, but it could perhaps be the only way out of the endless vicious circle of hate and counterhate that has transformed all of world history into an inhuman chain of battle and butchery.

C.F. von Weizsäcker suggests a third interpretation: an ethic of quiet self-assurance. It gives an attacker to understand: If you want to hit me in this brutal way, you are free to slap me on the other cheek as well, but know that you are not really affecting me!

A fourth explanation combines realism with morality. To offer the other cheek naturally brings with it the risk that one's opponent will strike a second time. But at the same time the hope persists that the victim's unresisting humility will overwhelm him, and that compassion or at least sympathy will win out in his heart.

Offering the other cheek, like offering the cloak, should be understood as a tacit appeal to the adversary's humanity—an appeal that can certainly claim a better prospect of success than can striking back angrily, as modern scientific research on aggression has in the meantime established.

This explanation finds confirmation from the mouth of a hardened practitioner of realpolitik, King Herod Agrippa II, who gave the same counsel to his compatriots in the following words: "Nothing softens the force of blows as much as bearing them patiently.

And the composure of the sufferers hinders thugs in their intentions." So we read in Flavius Josephus, who left no stone unturned in his effort to transform Roman violence into Roman tolerance. [36]

A fifth possibility involves the counsel of the prophet Jeremiah (whom Jesus repeatedly cites), who in similar circumstances reminds us that God loves the weak and shows mercy to the humble:

> It is a good thing for a man to carry the yoke in his youth. He sits alone and is silent when God lays it upon him and puts his mouth in the dust; perhaps there is still hope. He offers his cheek to the one who strikes him and lets himself be humiliated. For the Lord does not repudiate forever; he afflicts and again takes pity in his great kindness [Lam. 3:27–31].

Isaiah speaks in similar fashion, even of both cheeks: "I presented my back to those who beat me and my cheeks to those who boxed my ears" (Isa. 50:6).

Although Jesus' statement is reminiscent textually of these quotations from the prophets, we know that the Nazarene did not mean it literally. He proves that himself when a servant of the high priest strikes him in the face (John 18:22ff.) and he is justly angered by such abuse. When, a few years later, Paul is struck in the face (Acts 23:2), he goes still further: he impulsively flares up and curses his attacker.

PASSIVE RESISTANCE

I therefore suggest a sixth explanation, one that fits both Jesus' words and the historical circumstances. Understanding his advice in the sense of passive resistance, thousands of Jews followed Jesus, "turning the other cheek" on at least two occasions, and achieved more than all the insurrections and wars of the Zealots.

In the first incident, in the year 26, forbidden images of the "God-Caesar" had been brought to Jerusalem by night on Pilate's orders to deliberately violate the religious sensitivities of the Jews. Flavius Josephus reports:

> The Jews rose up against Pilate in Caesarea to ask him to take the images away from Jerusalem. . . . As Pilate refused, they

encamped around his house, staying there five days and five nights. On the sixth day Pilate went before his tribunal in the great stadium and called the Jews together under the pretext of wanting to respond to their wishes; then he gave armed soldiers the command to encircle the Jews. When the Jews saw how the soldiers surrounded them with a triple circle, they remained silent before this unexpected spectacle. Pilate, after declaring that he would have them killed if they would not honor the image of the emperor, gave the soldiers the sign to draw their swords. But the Jews threw themselves on the ground as if at a single command and offered their necks, all prepared to die rather than violate God's law. Overcome by this religious zeal, Pilate gave the command to take the images away from Jerusalem.[37]

To eliminate any doubts: Pilate's relationship to Caesar did not allow him to take up his office with a mass murder—a fact that he as well as all the Jews in Caesarea knew.

When, several years later, the emperor commanded Petronius, the Roman legate in Syria, to bring the statues of Caligula into the temple at Jerusalem, a general strike broke out. All fieldwork was discontinued and tens of thousands of Jews, from Galilean peasants to the royal house of Aristobulus, hastened to Tiberias to protest to the Romans that they would all die rather than permit the desecration of the temple. Impressed by the nonviolent solidarity of the Jews, Petronius gave way and himself became an advocate of Israel vis-à-vis the emperor, who died before he could enforce his worship on Israel.[38]

So things worked out in the beginning, thanks to theo-political wisdom, as Jesus fashioned nonviolence into political power, as Gandhi was able to do later in India and Martin Luther King, Jr., in Mississippi.

But the temptation to violence smoldered. The gospels are silent on just how the confrontation between Roman soldiers and Jesus' disciples came about, but it is not difficult to reconstruct. Judas Iscariot, the "daggerman," Simon the "Zealot," James and John, the "Sons of Thunder," and perhaps also Peter, the "man of rock," were, as Oscar Cullmann has shown, most probably Zealots or stood close to the Zealot philosophy. With a good third of his followers in the ideological camp of militant activists, Jesus preached nonviolent resistance to no avail. In vain were all his warnings that "all who seize the sword will perish by the sword"— no aphorism this, but a serious reference to the inexorable sword-justice of the Romans. And so it came to a clash, which would have meant inevitable defeat. The historic moment found its climax in three words: "Stop! No further!" (Luke 22:51).

Jesus wanted to liberate his people, not have them bleed to death. And when the misfortune that he tried so passionately to avoid but, as a skilled strategist, must have anticipated did in fact come, he was ready for the final step: "I am the one! Let these go" (John 18:8).

Judas betrayed him, Peter disowned him, and all the disciples failed him miserably. Nevertheless he took the burden on himself and assumed the responsibility for the bloodshed against which he had preached so tirelessly and so convincingly. And so he gave his life for his own and died the cruel, sacrificial death on the pagan cross in selfless certainty: "I have not lost any of those whom you gave me" (John 18:9).

In retrospect, one cannot help but admit that Jesus was right. Because the Jews did not take to heart his words "it is enough" (Luke 22:38), they came to "great distress, to a tribunal of anger, in which they fell by the . . . sword" (Luke 21:23–24) that they so heedlessly and rashly raised against the Roman superpower.

This would not have been difficult to foresee: it was the inevitable result of a short-sighted politics of confrontation. For if the land of Israel is a narrow landbridge between expansion-minded, more powerful nations—a feature of its historical destiny—then "confident tranquility and hope" (Isa. 30:15) and gentle-wise disarming love belong to the art of survival—in ancient times, in Jesus' day, and today as well.

It was the same deadly serious warning against flight into Zealot violence issued both by Isaiah (30:15ff.) and Flavius Josephus in his address to the people of Jerusalem (*The Jewish War,* V, 362–419) that Jesus sounded. Sadness, sorrow, and bitter disappointment brought tears to the eyes of the Nazarene when he had to proclaim to his holy city:

Oh, if you had (only) understood on this day what served your peace! But now it is (already) concealed from your eyes. For the days will (soon) come upon you when your enemies will . . . encircle you . . . and they will throw you and your children upon the ground and will leave in you not one stone upon another [Luke 19:41–44].

So the Jewish war ended with the fall of the Jewish state that, in its drive for independence, had fought to the end brave as a lion instead of acting "gently as a dove and wisely as a serpent"—as "the quiet ones in the land" had so urgently recommended and modeled in such an exemplary fashion.

If Israel had listened to those who counseled peace, one of whom was Jesus, and sought God's will in wise gentleness, Jerusalem would probably have been spared, the mass crucifixions would not have taken place, and perhaps the Jewish people would have been spared the national catastrophe of the year 70.

"But you did not wish it" (Matt. 23:37).

Looked at this way, the disarming love suggested by Jesus rests on six pillars that still offer food for thought to our generation:

First, it rests upon a realism that acknowledges the evil of this world as a fact. It eschews the illusionary, wishful thinking that insists on seeing only good everywhere and hopes to eliminate evil by passive silence. Jesus' realism accepts hostility as a fact—a fact that calls for change, a challenge to disarm those who act out of hatred.

Secondly, it harbors a deep faith in others, convinced that they are in a position to improve themselves and their environment. Hostility exists, but it need not always exist. Individuals can conquer their inclination toward hate and revenge. They can transform it into good, if they firmly resolve to do so.

Thirdly, it aims at the humanization of haters and the hated. The latter are not to be the scapegoats or whipping boys on whom I project my own mistakes, weaknesses, and sins, ultimately dehumanizing and demonizing the objects of my misdirected fault-finding. When I acknowledge the irrevocable humanity of opponents, they become human again in my attitude toward them. Then they too can rid themselves of the corrosive poison of hate and become capable of love and companionship again. In brief, disarming love struggles against enmity, not against the enemy.

Fourthly, its ideal is that *imitatio Dei* that Judaism considers the highest, the "royal" commandment: "Become holy, for I, your Lord, am holy" (Lev. 19:2). Our conduct should be a spotless mirroring of God; or at least an attempt to act as nobly as does God, to be as (humanly) all-embracing and understanding as God is (divinely). God's gracious love, of course, remains an ideal that no human can duplicate, but it remains a model for us to imitate at least fragmentarily day by day.

Fifthly, disarming love is not without its battles; it is a valiant love that does not avoid conflicts but takes its own stand. Its strategy is to build a bridge between legitimate self-love and practicable love of neighbor in the spirit of Leviticus 19:18 where *both* are commanded us: Love your neighbor as yourself. It is not a matter of "radical selflessness," which is indeed a psychological impossibility, nor threadbare sentimentalism, which for the most part contents itself with lip service, but of a reasonable combination of enlightened self-interest and practical altruism in which good will and complete sincerity weld the two together into a higher unity.

Last but not least, its tactic is a theo-politics of little, confidence-building steps—*away* from conflict, *toward* empathy; *away* from confrontation, *toward* cooperation; *away* from dogmatic monologue, *toward* a dialogue of equals. It is a long, toilsome trek of small acts, not of big words, for shalom is not to be had for a smaller price. Ultimately it is a matter of a worldly-wise, "serpent-clever" peace dynamic of self-conquest—of reconciliation and nonviolence that could effect a breakthrough to a world without enemies. Here is an undeluded utopianism, that even today has not lost an iota of its relevance. In fact, it has perhaps never been so relevant as today.

Chapter 14

REPARATION AND RESISTANCE
(Matt. 5:38–39a)

AN EYE FOR AN EYE, A TOOTH FOR A TOOTH

In connection with Jesus' far-reaching though not total rejection of violence, we must clarify the meaning of his seemingly suicidal instruction to practice passive self-surrender when confronted with evil (or an evil person), a directive that the Reformers objected to as impracticable.

You have heard that it was said, "An eye for an eye and a tooth for a tooth" [Matt. 5:38].

This verse is another instance of an abbreviated quotation from Jesus' Bible (Exod. 21:24). The evangelist has omitted the verb, giving the false impression that here is a charter for all the wronged to avenge themselves by repaying evil with evil. The reference here is to the "law of retaliation," as the church fathers labeled it, from which they could deduce "horrible retaliation-morality of Jews" and a "Jewish God of vengeance" to serve as an opaque background foil for the "Christian God of love."

As recently as 1963 the compilers of the original (French) edition of the *Jerusalem Bible* could still write: "We are forbidden to . . . return evil for evil, contrary to what is laid down by the Jewish *lex talionis*" (footnote to Matt. 5:39). The reference, of course, is to "an eye for an eye, a tooth for a tooth." The same phrase, with slight variations, is found three times in the Jewish Bible (Exod. 21:24; Lev. 24:20; Deut. 19:21).

When, after the Olympic murders of 1972 in Munich, Israel demanded of the German government that the self-confessed culprits be extradited, this biblical passage was used by German newspapers to characterize "retaliatory politics against Arabs" as "typically Old Testament."

Such an unbiblical distortion, which began in the early Middle Ages, is built on three errors of fact:

1) Revenge is expressly forbidden in the Hebrew Bible: "Be not vengeful . . . but love your neighbor as yourself" (Lev. 19:18). This commandment is clarified and reinforced by God's words: "Revenge is mine, says the Lord" (Deut. 32:35).

2) The original text reads: "But if there is danger to life, then *give* life for life, eye for eye, tooth for tooth. . . ." Thus the subject is *not* the injured person, entitled to take revenge or retaliation, but rather the injurer, who must offer reparation before a judge.

3) The key word in the Hebrew passage, *tachat*, does not mean "for" or "for the sake of," but "in place of." Martin Buber's translation is therefore true to both text and sense: "But if the worst happens, then give a life-compensation for life, eye-compensation for eye, tooth-compensation for tooth. . . ." In other words, the universal humanitarian rule of "measure for measure," which Jesus also recommended three times in the New Testament (Matt. 7:2; Mark 4:24; Luke 6:38) is elevated to the legal principle of pecuniary compensation for damages and pain in all cases of bodily injury.

It was in this single sense of satisfaction by compensation for damages that this Bible verse was understood and applied in Judaism long before Jesus, as the Talmud (Baba Kamma 83b; Kethuboth 38a) clearly proves. In the words of the Borromäus Bible: "The often misunderstood formula for the law of repayment (*lex talionis*) is a basis for judicial decisions, not a norm for person-to-person relationships."

The despised law of "retaliation" is thus a substantial step forward over against the desert ethic of prebiblical times, and the first substantial step toward a gradual refinement of human morality, which was later made explicit by the prophets of Israel and by Jesus.

What certain Christians still persist in pillorying as the prototype of Jewish retaliation-morality remains even today the juridical basis of reparation laws in the Christian West—a principle that the Jewish community elevated to a universal principle at a time when Teutons still slaughtered one another in tribal blood-vengeance and peopled their heaven with war gods.

But because Jesus most certainly knew his Bible better than did the final Greek editor of Matthew's Gospel, this distortion of the "law of retaliation" is rather to be attributed to the latter, who most probably also misunderstood Jesus' following statement.

HOW TO RESIST EVIL

And I say to you, do not resist the wicked [Matt. 5:39a].

Joachim Jeremias translates Matthew 5:39, "You should not carry on a lawsuit with someone who offends you." Adolf Schlatter also assumes that Jesus was thinking of a judicial procedure, so that verse 39 is thought to mean, "Do not file suit; do not invoke the protection of a judge." But neither the Greek wording nor a careful translation back into Jesus' mother tongue justifies this hypothesis.

Here Luther seems to demonstrate a better feeling for the text. He says straight out that Christians "with family ties" cannot practice such nonresistance, "for they are obligated to protect, defend, and shelter the others whenever they can" (*Wochenpredigten; Weimarer Ausgabe,* 32, 390).

Should Christians who are completely independent of such ties permit evil and injustice to go unopposed? Certainly not, according to Luther, who counseled "going to court and protesting against injustice, violence, etc., if only the heart is not false" (WA 32, 392).

In short, Luther taught very candidly that not even the most devout Christian may "accept injustice." "Out of a genuine love for righteousness" the Christian must refrain from observing this demand of the Instruction on the Mount (WA, ibid.).

Calvin counseled in the same direction; Christians should, "notwithstanding their friendly attitude toward their adversary, resort to the help of authority for the protection of their rights" (*Institutio*, IV, 20, 20).

I think that Jesus of Nazareth, if he did not himself formulate, would nevertheless have agreed with, this advice. We need only reflect soberly on what is supposedly expected here of persons like us. We are condemned to silent passivity, to handing ourselves over defenseless to the malicious, granting them an unobstructed pathway. Put concretely, a total repudiation of resistance means that a husband whose wife is raped before his eyes or whose children are killed in his presence should look on idly without even lifting a finger.

That would in fact be a formula for peace, but it would be a peace of the cemetery, in which the earth silently covers the good and the weak, and the violent triumph. But because it was Jesus' will to promote life as God's gift, and because he did not advocate any radicalism that could lead to loveless effects, he cannot have said, "Do not resist the wicked!"

I do not go as far as Dr. Franz Kamphaus, bishop of Limburg, who asserts that this warning against resistance has been "inserted by the evangelist." He is led to this conclusion because Jesus did not counsel his followers "to conduct themselves in a purely passive way, always to show no resistance."[39] Nevertheless I am convinced that this precept is indeed a foreign element in the Instruction on the Mount running counter to Jesus' entire ethics.

Five reasons speak against this text as given:

1) The nonresistance supposedly called for here would not be an appropriate intensification of the "law of retaliation" correctly understood. A more fitting counterpart would be a disclaimer of rights in the style of Solomon's advice: "Do not say, I will repay evil" (Prov. 20:22)—meaning: even if you are legally justified, renounce any claim that might look like retaliation.

2) In neither the Hebrew nor the Aramaic vocabulary of the first century do we find an equivalent for the Greek *antistenai* or "resist."

3) The passivity of this demand goes contrary to the course of this segment of the Instruction on the Mount, which encourages

disarmament by certain *actions*—offering one's cloak, going a second mile, and giving "to the person who asks you" (Matt. 5:42).

4) Renunciation of violence is not in any way identical with a renunciation of resistance, which, by abandoning neighbors who are victims of injustice, contributes to injustice and encourages victims to counterviolence. The love of neighbor that Jesus presupposes as a basic principle forbids one to stand by, immobile and tolerant, while the life, dignity, or security of one's neighbor is transgressed and undefended. "Do not stand by the blood of your neighbor" (Lev. 19:16), says Jesus' Bible in immediate connection with the commandment of love of neighbor (Lev. 19:18). Buber's translation is still clearer: "Do not take up an inactive stance at the blood of your comrade." To look on indifferently and passively when danger threatens a neighbor is, according to this passage, reprehensible and contrary to the ethos of the Bible.

The Talmud deduces, "Anyone who sees another drown in the river or dragged away by a predatory beast or threatened by robbers is obliged to rescue him" (Sanh 73a). The obligation to defend one's neighbor is emphasized still more in the rabbinic exegesis of the Bible passage that speaks of the atonement of a murder committed by an unknown hand. If a person is found slain and it is not known who was the killer, then, the Torah stipulates, the elders of the neighboring city should approach and they should commence by saying, "Our hands have not shed this blood and our eyes have seen nothing." And the Mishna adds, "Should the elders, then, be accused of shedding blood?" The passage has a different meaning. "Our hands have not shed this blood" means "It is not the case that this person has been within reach of our hands and we let this person go hungry." And "our eyes have seen nothing" is intended to say, "It is not the case that this person has been in our sight and abandoned by us." So the Talmudic statement means: those who do not take care of others and do not stand by them actively when their life is threatened, it is as if their own eyes had looked on.

Limited force employed not only in self-defense but also to ward off or soften the oppression of the weak can be the expression of selfless love of neighbor, a love that in essence fulfills the precept of Jesus' brother: "If you fulfill the royal law according to the Scripture, 'Love your neighbor as yourself,' then you do well" (James 2:8).

He calls the law of love of neighbor "royal" because in Jewish thought it enjoys an absolute precedence—before all other biblical statements, even those that command peacefulness and renunciation of force.

Jesus himself also confirmed it—so clearly and unambiguously that most theologians even today still do not deal with his express warning to his disciples, "Do not think that I have come to bring peace. I have not come to bring peace, but the sword" (Matt. 10:34). To the Hebrew mind this means that neither a bogus peace nor a hollow peace is worth the effort, and certainly not the enforced peace that the victor imposes on the vanquished, but only the realistic peace that is neither a guaranteed possession nor a soft pillow, but the fruit of tireless efforts and persistent struggles. Without a defensive sword true peace is simply not achievable.

On July 20, 1944, Dietrich Bonhoeffer was among those men and women who attempted to contain violence and defend countless "neighbors" from certain mass murder by forcibly removing Hitler. In their case nonviolence would have been an act of cowardice, of selfishness, of an indifferent abandonment of innocent fellow humans—in crass contradiction to the spirit of the entire Instruction on the Mount.

This is what Karl Rahner meant when he wrote:

> And yet so long as the age of this present world lasts justice, so sober, realistic, and hard as it seems, and even when it involves the use of power, whether in private or in public life, can precisely be the earthly form in which an extremely selfless love is embodied, which perhaps even for the sake of another may have to find courage enough to appear as though it were devoid of love.[40]

5) Renouncing resistance neither helps nor disarms "the wicked ones" who practice violence. On the contrary, it confirms them in their hostility and invites them, with impunity, to further violence. Passively tolerating evil deeds can only increase injustice, hand the poor and weak over to caprice and violence, and increase hatred of

neighbors—as the Third Reich and Hitler's "final solution" proved only too clearly.

But if Jesus did not say, "Do not oppose the wicked," what may he perhaps have said? In my search for Jesus' original phraseology I am struck by verse 8 of Psalm 37, which is echoed in no less than five other verses in the Instruction on the Mount (Matt. 3:9, 11, 21, 22, 29): "Do not compete in doing injustice." The second verb here *leharea*, has evidently been misread by the Greek translator as "the wicked," a common error that can be attributed to the lack of vowels in Hebrew orthography. The original text means: escape from the vicious circle of doing injustice, forever erupting into new injustices; break through the unsalutary escalation of mutual retaliation with its increasingly worse results; burst the "compulsions" that try to battle anxiety, suspicion, and mistrust through violence—do all this by gathering the courage to prevent evil and to disconcert the adversary by kindness.

It is not only evil that is contagious, but good as well. One need only try it! Jesus certainly does not mean compliance with the wicked, but victory over the wicked, whom you do not confront on their own turf but to whom you remain superior by battling injustice with justice, lies with truth, and violence with spirit. In a word: you are to be greater than evil—and evildoers—to overcome and survive both. Your being an innocent victim of murder will profit neither anyone on this earth nor the "living God," who "does not take pleasure in death, but in life" (Ezek. 18:23ff.)

Versed in Hebrew, Paul, the apostle to the gentiles who even "opposed" his fellow Christian Peter publicly to his face (Gal. 2:11ff.), presented the sense of Jesus' ethic better than did Matthew, and certainly earlier than any of the four evangelists. In the Letter to the Romans (12:21) he writes, "Do not let yourself be overcome by evil, but overcome evil with good."

Peter too conformed to his Lord's intention when, with the rabbis, he added that all hate is useless, harmful, and therefore unreasonable: "Because it is God's will that, through doing good, you will silence the ignorance of those who do not understand" (1 Pet. 2:15). Seen in depth, all hatred is groundless, and therefore utterly stupid. Here is a dual piece of advice, concurring both with courteous, disarming love and also with the nonviolent resistance of turning the other cheek, but without foregoing human dignity, self-defense, or one's own freedom of action.

In short, what Jesus means and probably also said is, "Resist evil—in kindness." However one may explain the original text, an invitation to suicide is no more to be inferred from the Instruction on the Mount than is radical pacifism to be wrested from the Bible.

Epilogue

UTOPIA OR
PROGRAM FOR ACTION?

It is remarkable how close the Instruction on the Mount is to the Letter of Jesus' brother James, which Martin Luther labeled "a really insipid epistle." At the heart of both writings stands the radical commandment of love as the "royal law of love of neighbor" (James 2:8), which leads inevitably to dedication to the poor—preference for the unloved, and emphasis on the performance of works of love as the acid test of faith.

In Deuteronomy 15:4 it is promised that "there will be no poor among you in Israel." But shortly thereafter the admission that "there are always poor in the land" (Deut. 15:11) turns the focus back to reality. To bridge this chasm the Torah commands, "Open your hand to your brother who is in need and is poor in your land" (Deut. 15:11).

For Jesus, however, those "in need" also include the hated and their haters, for they, just like the poor, need practical love—not a verbalization of sympathy, but an outstretched hand. Hate corrodes the heart of the hater even before it touches the hated. So it is incumbent on the latter to transform the vicious circle of hatred into an angelic circle of empathy by acts of love. Give your haters tangible proof that you wish to help them so that there is no reason for them to hate you.

Political realists, of course, will say that such disarming love, which goes hand in hand with care for the poor, has no place in international conflicts. It is strictly a matter for individuals or small groups, not large collectivities.

Correct, Jesus concedes between the lines, but if my disciples do not make a start so that others will be stimulated to imitate them, everything will remain as it is, and humanity will destroy itself.

The practitioners of so-called realpolitik in all ages shrug their shoulders: it is wearisome to debate with utopians. So we listen politely and the matter is disposed of. A few have had pangs of conscience and have added: the challenges of the Instruction on the Mount are so lofty that only Jesus himself could fulfill them. But he did so as representative for the entire world, so that we, through faith in him, share in the fruit of his accomplishment.

To this argument of faith Jesus answers clearly, "Not everyone who says to me 'Lord, Lord' will enter God's realm, but only the one who *does* the will of my Father in heaven" (Matt. 7:21)—a teaching that he once again at the end of the Instruction on the Mount drums into the sluggish who would rather listen noncommittally than put into practice:

Everyone who hears these my words and does them can be compared to a clever man who built his house on rock. And rain poured down and the floods came and the winds blew and pushed against that house, and it did not collapse, because it was grounded on rock. And everyone who hears these my words and does not do them can be compared to a foolish man who built his house on sand. And the rain poured down and the floods came and the winds blew and pushed against that house and it collapsed [Matt. 7:24–27].

If this is the case, then well-intentioned sermons are no more effective than their attentive audiences, unless implementation of this teaching follows. Jesus surely meant this too when he in the end charged his disciples to make followers of "all peoples," teaching them to hold "all I have commanded" (Matt. 28:19–20). (The Greek text here is clearly directed to "pagan peoples.")

The fact that even today these words find a hearing but very little heeding seems surely to be related to the fact that this Instruction on the Mount is permeated with political implications alongside which the French, American, and Russian revolutions pale into insignificance—political in the full sense of active participation in the management of society, and revolutionary in the sense of a radical alteration of all authority structures in order to replace old bondings with a completely new form of human interrelationship.

Political as well was the execution of Jesus, who was condemned and crucified by the Romans as a political messianic pretender. That this did not necessarily imply anti-Roman or military activity is proved by the earlier execution of the politically innocuous John the Baptist; he too had called forth a religious mass movement that everyone interested in the protection of the political status quo ultimately had to recognize as revolutionary. For if the poor, the gentle, and the persecuted are called happy, if nonviolence wins out, if mammon is devalued (Matt. 6:24), and no one should judge one's neighbor any longer (Matt. 7:1), what happens to authority structures, civil obedience, police control, and jurisprudence?

Homo homini lupus, according to the power-loving Romans. Hell, says Jean-Paul Sartre, is other people.

The Jewish Bible, on the other hand, is convinced that everyone is capable of giving everyone else a foretaste of the heavenly realm. In this sense Jesus' Instruction on the Mount is his answer to the biblical challenge to climb to the peak of the Torah ideal: an end to anger, cursing, and estrangement; a final break with hatred, envy, and retaliation, and a clear path to the divine commandment of love as the center of the Torah, a guide to its fulfillment, and a key to the gate of the heavenly realm.

The luminaries of the Jewish Middle Ages agree: one need not die, says Maimonides, to be able to hallow God and God's dominion, even if the martyr's death does represent the highest level of sanctity. Asceticism and death are not the goal of Jewish self-sanctification. As Maimonides writes:

> They who avoid sin and fulfill the commandments for no other reason than love of God—not out of fear of punishment and not to boast about it—they who are friendly and amiable to their fellow humans, who suffer insults without themselves insulting others, who act respectfully to those who treat them slightingly, whose relationship with others is loving, they hallow the name of God publicly [*Jessode Ha-Torah*, 5].

Jesus erred in expecting the great beginning of the era of God's visible dominion within the near future. Neither a new order of things nor manifest redemption entered on the stage of world history. And he did not always hold to his own Instruction on the Mount. His angry philippic against his adversaries (Matt. 23:13–38) reminds us of the holy zeal of the prophets, far from either reconciliation (Matt. 5:22-25) or disarming love.

And yet! When things moved to a final confrontation, and neither the cleverness of a serpent nor the wisdom of practical experience could save him, he remained master of the situation. He did not lower himself to the norms of the despot. Like every great teacher in Judaism, he imposed heavier duties on himself than he ever demanded of his disciples.

Half sadly, half resigned, he said to his own in parting, "Greater love than this has no one, to give up one's life for one's friends" (John 15:13). And shortly thereafter his words were followed by the heroic deed of faith. Self-sacrifice of this sort had never been demanded or even recommended by him for anyone else. It attests to a spiritual nobility that is the special possession of the ethical elite who do not need inspirational sermons.

And so he proved himself not only a "teaching master" but also a "life master," to use Meister Eckhart's terms. The first instructs through intelligent speech, sensitivity, and pedagogy. Decidedly more is expected of the "life master": not only knowledge but wisdom; not only insight, but charisma; not only rhetoric, but the art of living from an inner unity of teaching and life, of word and deed. For in the end, the words of an American poet are true of all great teachers:

> I'd rather see a sermon
> than hear one any day;
> I'd rather one should walk with me
> than merely tell the way.
> The eye's a better pupil and more willing
> than the ear,
> Fine counsel is confusing,
> but example's always clear;
> And the best of all the preachers are the men
> who live their creeds,
> For to see good put in action
> is what everbody needs.

EDGAR A. GUEST

And so Jesus washes his disciples' feet; he practices nonviolence when he is apprehended; to avoid bloodshed he takes the full blame upon himself at Gethsemani; he suffers ridicule in silence; humbly he offers his attacker "the other cheek"; in the face of his accusers he remains mute and desists from self-defense; on the cross he still consoles his companions in suffering, and even at the threshold of death he dares to hope, despite all his despair. To the end he remains true to himself and his faith, departing this life with words of forgiveness for his enemies. The First Letter of Peter presents Jesus as an "example" for his community: "He was defamed, but did not defame; he suffered but did not threaten; he left it all to the God who judges justly" (2:23).

The moral is obvious: without the passion and crucifixion, the Instruction on the Mount would remain an eloquent, though demanding, axiological sermon. It gets its true binding force only through the exemplary life, sufferings, and death of the Nazarene who sealed its validity with his own blood. Indeed, by his fruits you will recognize him!

The Instruction on the Mount, like all four Gospels in their entirety, belongs of course to a determinate historical hour notable for the crisis it faced. But is that to say that this historical anchoring robs it of relevance today?

Martin Buber answers this question:

> [The biblical word] is not to be detached from the situation in which it is spoken. . . . A precept is not an aphorism but an exhortation addressed to the people and always heard by later generations as spoken to this particular generation, never as something elevated to the timeless. To make it into an aphorism is to convert . . . the urgency of hearing into the detachment of interested reading—whereby it loses its flesh and blood.[41]

And nevertheless everything speaks for the fact that today as hardly ever before, the Instruction on the Mount is persuasive in our hour of world history. The so-called balance of terror, the constantly growing nuclear armament of the superpowers, and the long since achieved capability of the human race to commit global suicide—these apocalyptic facts trumpet the relevance of the Instruction on the Mount for our day.

Are not the arms race, East-West rivalry, North-South disparity, and the 138 military confrontations since 1945 like the "floods that came" and the "storms that blew on that house, so that it collapsed" (Matt. 7:27)? Is our time not characterized precisely as Jesus' by threats of catastrophes, by doubt, and an almost convulsive search for solid foundations?

Anyone pondering the final consequence of our contemporary political and military configurations can scarcely help acknowledging the reasonableness of the ethos of the Instruction on the Mount, which holds the interests of one's opponent equal to one's own. Quite unreasonable, on the other hand, are the egotism everywhere taken for granted, the arms race, the ancient friend-and-foe mentality, and the balancing of "as you do to me, I will do to you!"

Reason today dictates carrying the Golden Rule out of the houses of God into parliaments and foreign-affairs offices: "Everything that you wish others to do to you, do also to them" (Matt. 7:12)—from social welfare through disarmament conferences to the settling of international conflicts. For today the love of neighbor and the ministry of reconciliation are not platitudes or mere embellishment of a pious sermon, but the urgent dictates of an urgently needed strategy of conciliation.

One world—or none!

Life peaceably—or die!

Do away with war before it does away with us!

This is the clear-cut alternative increasingly thrust, with shattering force, upon the dwellers of Planet Earth.

The Bible too confronts us with the age-old choice between good and evil, curse and blessing, hate and love. In these circumstances Jesus' Instruction on the Mount, rightly understood, can be the foundation for a strategy of humane survival and the guidepost for world peace.

The world clock sounds the passing hours. Our time of probation is running out. It is already late.

NOTES

1. *Pocket Gandhi Series no. 6*, Bombay, 1963, pp. 43, 65.

2. Ibid., p. 44.

3. Karl Marx, *Gesamtausgabe*, I, 246.

4. Günther Bornkamm, *Jesus of Nazareth* (New York: Harper, 1960), pp. 222–23.

5. Karl Barth, *Church Dogmatics*, II, 2, 688f.

6. Gerhard Kittel, *Theologisches Wörterbuch zum Neuen Testament;* English trans. *Theological Dictionary of the New Testament*, (Grand Rapids: Eerdmanns, 1964-1976).

7. Martin Luther, "Table Talk," *Weimarer Ausgabe* (WA), I, 524f.

8. Leo Baeck, *The Essence of Judaism* (New York: Schocken, 1961, reprint of 1948), p. 73.

9. Luther, "Table Talk," WA 32, 356.

10. Ibid., 11, 259.

11. John Calvin, *Institutes of the Christian Religion*, II, 8, 7.

12. Nicholas of Lyra, *Postilla super NT* (on Matthew 5:20f).

13. W. Bauer, *Wörterbuch zum Neuen Testament*, 1331-33; Eng. ed. *A Greek-English Lexicon of the New Testament and Other Early Christian Literature* (Chicago: University of Chicago Press, 1979).

14. See Aboth II, 1-2.

15. See, e.g., Tos Yota VI, II; Tos Pess. VIII, 21.

16. *Basic Writings of Nietsche*, ed. Walter Kaufman (New York: Modern Library, 1968), p. 470.

17. Charlotte Klein, *Anti-Judaism in Christian Society* (Philadelphia: Fortress, 1978).

18. Dietrich von Oppen, *Das personell Zeitalter* (Gütersloh, 1967),p.11.

19. Joseph Ruppert Geiselmann, "Jesus Christus," in *Handbuch Theologischer Grundbegriffe* (Munich, 1962), I, 747.

20. Ethelbert Stauffer, *Die Botschaft Jesu damals und heute* (Bern, 1959), pp. 27f.

21. E.g., Mekhilta Ex Jethro 9; Tos Yota VI, 6-11; Tos Bik I,2.

22. Herman Rauschning, *Gespräche mit Hitler* (Zurich, 1934)

23. In J. Schniewind, *Nachgelassene Reden und Aufsätze* (1952), p. 26.

24. Flavius Josephus, *The Jewish War*, II, 8, 6.

25. Adolf Holl, *Jesus in Bad Company* (New York: Holt, Rinehart, Winston, 1973), pp. 30–31.

26. S.R. Hirsch, *Gesammelte Schriften* (Frankfurt, 1920), II, 187–202.

27. Stauffer, *Die Botschaft Jesu,* p. 126.

28. Ibid., p. 146.

29. Ibid.

30. Jules Isaac, *Jesus and Israel* (New York: Holt, Reinhart, Winston, 1971), p. 400.

31. Leo Baeck in T. Bevet, *Angst-Sicherung Geborgenheit* (Bielefeld, 1975).

32. Leonhard Ragaz, *Die Bergpredigt Jesu* (Bern, 1979), p. 92.

33. In the Church of St. Paul., Frankfurt, Oct. 16, 1977.

34. See my study of the imperial tax in *Ex predigte in ihren Synogogen* (Gütersloh, 1980), pp. 34–53.

35. Baeck, *Essence of Judaism,* I, 157

36. Josephus, *Jewish War,* II, 16, 4.

37. Ibid., II, 16, 4.

38. Josephus, *Antiquities of the Jews,* XVIII, 8.

39. Franz Kamphaus in *Die christliche Friendensbotschaft,* Arbeitshilfe, n. 28 (Bonn: German Bishops Conference, 1982), p.50.

40. Karl Rahner, "The Peace of God and the Peace of the World," *Theological Investigations* 10 (New York: Crossroad/Seabury, 1973), p. 389.

41. Martin Buber, *Die Schrift und ihre Verdeutschung* (1936), pp. 312f.

SCRIPTURE INDEX

Compiled by James Sullivan

Other Orbis Titles . . .

THE BEATITUDES
To Evangelize as Jesus Did
by Segundo Galilea

An inspirational treatment of the Beatitudes of both Luke and Matthew by a popular writer of spirituality.

"Long experience in pastoral activity has qualified Galilea, one of Latin America's best known theologians, to direct others on the way to spiritual maturity. His message is written in a style that makes sense to anyone, lay or expert, ready to give assent to the radical challenge of the Gospel."

Spirituality Today

no. 344-9 128pp. pbk. $5.95

FOLLOWING JESUS
by Segundo Galilea

What does it really mean to follow Jesus? Segundo Galilea, a Catholic priest working among the grassroots in Santiago, Chile, uses portions of scripture to reveal the Jesus we seek to follow. Galilea presents a vision of the Christian life that unites personal faith and commitment to the exploited poor.

no. 136-5 128pp. pbk. $6.95

SPIRITUALITY OF THE BEATITUDES
Matthew's Challenge for First World Christians
by Michael H. Crosby

"A powerful book that integrates much that too often is separated: spirituality and the Scriptures, prayer and ministry, piety and justice, the personal and the communal. This Capuchin author has thoroughly appropriated both the themes of this gospel and its recent scholarly interpretations. The

reflective theology which results is a biblical spirituality both informative and formative that speaks to the reordering of relationships and structures in society and in the church." *National Catholic Reporter*
no. 465-8   254pp. pbk. $7.95

GOD'S KINGDOM
A Guide for Biblical Study
by George V. Pixley
Foreword by Harvey Cox

"At last we have a book that analyzes the vital connections between political economy and religious faith in all the major periods of biblical history. Compactly and clearly written, with abundant biblical references, Pixley's work will be a tremendous asset for study groups that want to grasp the Bible as a resource for social change." *Norman K. Gottwald*

"A provocative volume, ideal for those doing serious scripture study in the context of liberation." *Religious Education*

George Pixley is professor of Old Testament at the Seminario Bautista in Mexico City.
no. 156-X   116pp. pbk. $5.95

BIBLE OF THE OPPRESSED
by Elsa Tamez

Elsa Tamez, professor of biblical studies in San José, Costa Rica, examines nine Hebrew words for oppression in the Old Testament and in each case asks: what understanding of oppression is conveyed by the word, who are the agents of oppression, who are the objects, and what are the methods used to oppress? She relates the biblical story of oppression and liberation to the contemporary Latin American scene.
no. 035-0   88pp. pbk. $5.95

THE BIBLE AND LIBERATION
Political and Social Hermeneutics
edited by Norman K. Gottwald

A collection of twenty-eight essays that attempt to explain and demonstrate biblical interpretation from a socio-political perspective. Contributors include noted scholars Walter Brueggemann, Elisabeth Schüssler-Fiorenza, George Pixley, Carlos Mesters, Luise Schottroff, Juan Luis Segundo, and others committed to focusing on the life and struggles of the communities that shaped and were shaped by the Bible.

"In biblical studies such an orientation is presently raising the most stimulating questions and producing the most exciting and challenging results. This volume will serve as a first-rate introduction to the methods and results of socio-political biblical study."   *Homiletic*

Norman Gottwald is W.W. White Professor of Biblical Studies at New York Theological Seminary and the author of *The Tribes of Yahweh* (Orbis, 1979).

no. 044-X   **624pp. pbk.**   **$18.95**

THE TRIBES OF YAHWEH
A Sociology of the Religion of Liberated Israel, 1250–1050, B.C.E.
by Norman K. Gottwald

"In this massive work on the sociology of religion in premonarchic ancient Israel, Gottwald meticulously examines the biblical theories of such scholars as Noth, von Rad, Alt, and Mendenhall and sociological and historical-cultural views of Durkheim, Marx, and Weber to define such concepts as tribalism, social structure, and the cultic-ideological and tradition history in the various books of the Bible. He discusses the social systems and economic modes of the other peoples of the Near East and compares the ancient Israelite social structure to the Greek city states. The comprehensiveness of this work in using primary as well as secondary sources makes it a valuable scholarly contribution to the study of this period." *Library Journal*

no. 499-2   **944pp. pbk.**   **$19.95**

GOD OF THE LOWLY
Socio-Historical Interpretations of the Bible
Willy Schottroff and Wolfgang Stegemann, Eds.
trans. by Matthew J. O'Connell

A German theological best-seller now available in translation from Orbis. Stegemann, Solle, Luise and Willy Schottroff, and other members of the rising "materialist school" of biblical interpretation in Europe elaborate their method and expose the Bible's partiality for the weak, the underprivileged, and the poor.

"These essays combine the expected German thoroughness in critical exegesis with an acute analysis of social context to build 'a bridge of love' between our world and the biblical world. This is an important contribution to a liberating knowledge of scripture."   *Norman K. Gottwald*
no. 153-5   176pp. pbk. $9.95

MY ENEMY IS MY GUEST
Jesus and Violence in Luke
by J. Massyngbaerde Ford

For this noted scholar, Luke differs dramatically from his predecessors in portraying Jesus as an advocate of nonviolence. Into the "seething cauldron" of first-century Palestine comes Luke's Jesus, whose approach to pacifism confounds even his peace-making contemporaries: he forgives and loves enemies. A signal contribution to Lukan redactional studies. Must reading for biblical scholars and all Christians opposing the arms race.

". . . an excellent, lively, and timely book."   *David Daube,*
University of California, Berkeley

J. Massyngbaerde Ford is the author of the Anchor Bible Commentary on Revelation.
no. 348-1   192pp. pbk. $9.95